The Quickening Pulse

The Quickening Pulse

Books 1–5

to accompany
Excellence in English Books 1–5

The Quickening Pulse

Book 4

Selected by D J Brindley

HODDER AND STOUGHTON

LONDON SYDNEY AUCKLAND TORONTO

ISBN 0 340 23770 8

First published 1979

Selection copyright © 1979 D J Brindley

R.P.

Contents

The Man who wasn't Scared	*Andrew Garve*	1
Mountain Madness	*Tom Hopkinson*	6
Johnny One-Eye	*Damon Runyon*	14
Playing with Fire	*D J Brindley*	27
Tony Kytes	*Thomas Hardy*	34
And Man	*William Saroyan*	43
Death of the Zulu	*Uys Krige*	52
The Rocking-Horse Winner	*D H Lawrence*	61
Mr Kaplan's White Banner	*Leo Rosten*	76
The Verger	*Somerset Maugham*	83
First Confession	*Frank O'Connor*	91
The Bottomless Well	*Walter S Terry*	100
To Build a Fire	*Jack London*	114

The Man who wasn't Scared

by Andrew Garve

It was in September 1957, shortly before my retirement as Chief Constable of Downshire, that the man who was soon to become notorious as the 'Downshire Terror' first showed his hand. A chap named John Iles, a driving instructor employed by the Excelsior School of Motoring in Donchester, had been to the pictures after work and had left his car parked in a quiet run-in beside the School's premises, as he usually did. When he went to collect it just before ten o'clock he found that someone had torn off a headlamp, forced a door and slashed the upholstery. On the driver's seat there was a cutting from the *Donchester Herald* reporting a court case in which Iles had recently been involved—one of his pupils had panicked during a lesson and mounted the pavement before the dual control could be used, slightly injuring a woman. Pinned to the cutting was a piece of paper on which the wrecker had pencilled in block capitals: FIFTEEN KILLED AND 112 INJURED IN ROAD ACCIDENTS IN DOWNSHIRE LAST MONTH! NO WONDER, WITH MEN LIKE YOU IN CHARGE OF NEW DRIVERS! WHY DON'T YOU PAY ATTENTION WHEN YOU'RE ON THE JOB? IF IT HAPPENS AGAIN, YOU'LL BE FOR IT!

It was an ugly little incident, and we did all we could to discover who was responsible. But there wasn't much to go on. The job must have been done after dark, for no-one had seen anyone near the car. The wrecker had evidently worn gloves, for there were no useful fingerprints. The paper on which the message had been written was common typing paper, unwatermarked, and could have been bought at any stationer's. The message itself afforded no clue, except that it pointed to a reasonably literate person. We interviewed a number of people who might conceivably have had a private grudge against Iles, including the woman who had been knocked down by the School car, the pupil who had mounted the pavement, and several others who had failed to pass their driving test after tuition—but we got nowhere. Iles himself was very upset by

I

the incident, and the School had to give him some sick leave.

We were still working on the case when, a few days later, the first murder was committed. A young man named Jocelyn Wade, a member of a well-to-do county family, had been up to London for the day in his fast sports car, and on his way back had dropped into a quiet country pub, the Dog and Feathers, about five miles beyond Donchester. He had left the pub just before ten—and at ten-thirty his body had been found lying beside his car in the car park. His skull had been crushed by two blows from a heavy instrument, possibly a spanner, delivered by someone who must have crept up behind him. On the car seat, the murderer had left a sheet of typing paper, with the pencilled words: THIS MAN DROVE THROUGH DONCHESTER HIGH STREET AT 42 M.P.H. THIS EVENING. WATCH OUT, YOU DOWNSHIRE SPEED FIENDS! IT MAY BE YOUR TURN NEXT! Once again, there were no fingerprints, no material clues. Once again, the assault had taken place in darkness, and the assailant had got clear away.

We knew now that there was a maniac in our midst—a man with his own crazy notion of a road safety campaign. Next morning the activities of the 'Downshire Terror' were the chief topic of conversation all over the country. The popular newspapers were full of him. Hordes of reporters arrived in Donchester, virtually taking over the County Hotel. They wanted to know not merely what we were doing about the Wade murder, but how we proposed to prevent any more deaths. On that point, it wasn't very easy to be reassuring. The peculiar grimness of all these multiple-murder cases, where sudden attacks are made out-of-doors after dark and no personal motive links the murderer and victim, is that the police usually have to wait for further attacks before they can close their net. What I did say was that one of the best safeguards might well be for everyone to drive with exceptional care in Downshire until the Terror was apprehended.

It seemed certain that we should need outside help in our task, and I had already asked for a conference at the Home Office to concert plans. But before it could be held, there was a second murder. This time the victim was a woman, a Mrs Fray. She had been visiting friends in Donchester and had set off home in her car soon after nine o'clock. At ten she had been found lying beside the car on a grass verge, not far from her house, with her head battered in. The usual piece of paper on the driving seat said: THIS WOMAN FAILED TO STOP AT THE HALT SIGN IN DONCHESTER THIS AFTER-NOON. The front near-side tyre of her car was flat, but there was no puncture—the valve cap had been removed and the valve loosened. It seemed probable that the Terror had marked her down during the day, followed her to her friend's house, loosened the valve in the street after dark, and assaulted her on the road home when the flat tyre had forced her to stop.

The new murder gave even greater urgency to the conference at the Home Office. It was attended by several experienced officers from the Yard and by the Chief Constables of the counties adjoining Downshire. They were all short-handed, for like Downshire their territories lay between London and the sea and at this time of the year the crowded state of the roads and the frequent accidents were a heavy strain on police manpower. However, they agreed that reinforcements for Downshire were essential. The best hope seemed to lie in greatly strengthened night patrols, so that even if the next murder couldn't be prevented we should at least have early information on which to act. The Terror, after his butchering excursions, must have a lot of blood on him, and his first need would be to rush off to some quiet retreat where he could remove all traces. Our aim must be to intercept him. Our counter-measures included dividing the county up into sections with a system of road checks that could be brought instantly into operation. We also fixed up a decoy plan, by which plain clothes men in private cars would drive around the built-up areas of the county at more than the legal limit in the hope that the Terror would eventually follow one of them.

For a week after the conference, nothing happened. Then the Terror suddenly struck again—and this time it was in broad daylight! A lorry driver named Albert Stokes had stopped his vehicle in a lay-by some ten miles outside the county boundary, and after lunch had stretched out in his cab for a nap. He was found there in the middle of the afternoon, dead from multiple head injuries. The message on the seat said: THIS MAN

PASSED ME IN DONCHESTER AT 32 M.P.H. HIS LEGAL LIMIT IS 20 M.P.H.

It was now clear that the Terror, though still concentrating on what happened in Downshire, was prepared to pursue his victim outside the county if necessary. That meant that every driver who passed through was taking a risk, unless he drove impeccably. The odds against any one person being picked on were, of course, considerable, but by now the word 'Downshire' had become synonymous in the public mind with sudden, violent death, and most people preferred not to take chances. There was no great falling off in the amount of traffic, but there was a marked improvement in road behaviour and an impressive observance of all speed limits. At this rate, the Terror would soon be short of victims.

Another week went by—a week of unremitting inquiry into the earlier incidents and of ceaseless vigilance by the road patrols. By now, a huge force of police had been drafted into the area. As one quiet day followed another, I began to think that the Terror had abandoned his campaign. Any sane person would certainly have been deterred by our preparations. But late one night, he killed again. His victim, a man named Lever, was found with the usual head injuries only a short time after the assault. His car was in a ditch in an unfrequented lane, and it looked as though he had driven it there himself. The message on the seat said: THIS MAN WAS DRUNK IN CHARGE! Within seconds of the discovery, our machinery went smoothly into action, and we must have missed the escaping murderer by the narrowest of margins.

We brought in yet more police and increased the patrols. For nearly a fortnight, Downshire waited in a state of mounting tension. Then, suddenly—and in a way I hadn't foreseen—the end came.

I was driving home one night, very tired after a late conference at the station. I had just turned into the High Street when a small black car passed me. For a moment I could hardly believe my eyes, for it was doing over 40 m.p.h. in a restricted area—and drivers in Downshire simply didn't do that sort of thing any longer! Then I decided that it must be one of my decoys. I put on speed until I could read the number. I knew all the decoy numbers, and it wasn't one of them.

I stepped hard on the accelerator, and so did the chap in front. Two other police cars swung in from side turnings and joined in the chase. We raced through the town at sixty miles an hour, and I passed the black car at sixty-five. Its brakes squealed as I slowed down in front of it, there was a crash as it hit me, and then it swerved off the road through a garden fence. As it stopped the driver jumped out and began to run. I gave chase, and so did half a dozen other officers, and we caught him in less than fifty yards.

It was the driving instructor, John Iles! He was wearing a long plastic raincoat, and there was blood all over it. He'd just done his last job!

We found out afterwards that he'd been spending his 'sick leave' in a caravan, parked beside a stream in a lonely spot in the next county. After each murder, he'd gone straight back there to clean up. He told us that he felt that his mission in Downshire was now pretty well accomplished and that he'd intended to return to work on the following day. So if he hadn't been the one man in Downshire who wasn't scared of the Terror, he might have got away with it.

He was hopelessly mad, of course. If his deeds hadn't made that clear, his attitude in court would have done. According to him, he was a public benefactor and should have had a medal. He admitted he'd killed five people, but he pointed out that in the month in which he'd been operating, road casualties in Downshire had fallen from 15 dead and 112 injured to 7 dead and 43 injured, solely on account of him—a net saving of 8 lives and much useless suffering. The judge said grimly that this was the arithmetic of bedlam, and had him bundled off to Broadmoor without any more fuss.

There was exuberant relief throughout Downshire when it was realised that sanity had returned to the county and that the danger was over. The next month's road casualty figures were an all-time record at 20 killed and 133 injured.

Mountain Madness *by Tom Hopkinson*

We were staying at the Hope of Deliverance up in Westmorland—an inn which climbers know as well as they know their own front-door steps. There were about a dozen of us there, and we were gathered—where everybody always gathered at the Hope—in Joe Calpin's kitchen.

After a while, as you may suppose, the eternal question came up—who was the best climber each of us had ever known?

We all said our say, and at last it came to landlord Joe. 'The finest climber I ever knew,' he said, 'was a man I wouldn't climb with for a thousand pounds.'

Everyone sat up a bit at that, while old Joe, knowing that he'd got the company's attention, began to fill his pipe. And here's the tale, pretty much as Joe told it.

Nowadays you very seldom see idiots in the mountains. What I mean to say is—not everyone who comes here is a famous climber, but they're pretty well all up to whatever job they tackle. They wear sensible clothes, they study the lie of the land, they ask advice from anyone that knows better than themselves, and they don't take on something difficult till they're ready for it.

In the old days things were different. You'd get fellows coming up here straight out of offices, wearing their city suits and bowler hats, with thin shoes on their feet that'd be wet through before they got here, and cut to pieces by the time they'd walked down to the bottom of the garden. You may laugh, but it's true. I've see 'em here, in this inn, many a time.

Two of our worst 'mountain lunatics' (as my father used to call them) turned up the day before Good Friday . . . about thirty, or maybe thirty-five years ago. Busson—their name was, John and James Busson. They were in their early twenties—clerks in some solicitor's office down in Manchester.

Now, about that time there was a big tradition of climbing among professional folk round Manchester, and I fancy these two young fellows thought they were doing something rather smart in 'going climbing'—just like their boss and his friends.

6

I dare say, too, they'd heard him speak of the mountains in an exciting kind of way. They expected a bit more of a thrill here than they got going off to Southport or Buxton, or wherever they usually went.

The two had a small suitcase with them, and we supposed they'd have proper clothes in that, so we said nothing when they landed up in full rig-out, black coats and waistcoats, shining collars and cuffs, pointed shoes—or boots I suppose it was in those days.

Next morning was the kind of day we often have up here in spring, blue sky and sunshine early on, then it comes all over cloudy about eleven, with the afternoon stormy, and a few minutes of brightness later when the sun goes down.

'Splendid morning,' said one of the Bussons to my father, who came in to speak to them. (They were still wearing the same clothes.)

'Ah! Looks all right now,' father answered, 'but it'll be blowing later on.'

'Oh no, I don't think so. Looks to me as though it would be fine right over the holidays. That's what they were saying down in Manchester. Fine all over Easter, they were saying.'

Father kept quiet. Then the other Busson chipped in. 'We're going for a climb today,' he explained. 'Over Blue Mell, on to High Stones, and down into Long Rigg for the night. We thought that would make a good day's going.'

'It would,' said my father. 'It would make a very good day's going for strong walkers. But you're not going to try it in those clothes.'

He didn't say that as a question. He just said it like I put it, as though no-one could be as barmy as all that.

'Why not?' asked the first. 'All right, aren't they? No objection to them?'

'We don't believe in dressing up,' said the second.

Well, father talked to them for a bit, but it was no good. They'd bought the district for four days with their return-tickets, and they meant to make full use of it.

When father saw how matters were, he shut up, but he told 'em one thing—enough to make sure nothing serious happened. 'If you've any trouble on Blue Mell,' he said, 'don't go up onto the Stones: take the path that runs down from the cairn on

7

Blue Mell, to the left. It's an easy way and a pleasant walk. It brings you down into Sledmere, where there's a farm for you to stay.'

Well, they looked at father much as any of you would look at me if I told you there was a nice walk up the hill behind the church, and about half an hour later they set off. They were still wearing the same outfit and they were carrying the suitcase on a stick between 'em.

That same evening a good few parties turned up, the place was packed, and we gave no more thought to our two lunatics. We supposed they'd been worn out after the first five miles, and taken father's advice and gone down into Sledmere. Then they'd have made their way to a station and gone off to spend their last two day's holiday in Southport.

But on Tuesday morning, when they should have been back at work, we had a wire from their office, asking where they were. Father got together all the guests there were still about the place, and we set off up Blue Mell to look for them. We came upon one, just as it was getting dark. We got him down here—with that stretcher you see in the corner—and a day or two later he told us what had happened. . . .

They'd set off from here that morning, the pair of them, as jolly as you please. They walked about a mile up the lane and thought there was nothing in this climbing business. 'You could take a kid up, here,' said one.

Then they got out on to the fell, and began to find the going a bit steep. Their boots pinched, their ankles were sore, their calves and thighs ached. They'd pains in the small of their backs, and as they got a bit higher one of them even began to say he felt dizzy—and all the time they'd got that suitcase to sweat along between 'em, or rather in turns, for it's a narrow track and they couldn't walk side by side.

It took 'em about three and a half hours to do the six-odd miles to the top of Blue Mell, and they were never more delighted than when they saw that cairn. They sat down on it and ate most of the sandwiches father'd made them take, and after talking it over, they decided to follow his advice and go down to Sledmere. It was about the only sensible thing they did that day—and even that they didn't really do.

'We don't want just to walk straight down,' said John (he

8

was the one that had felt dizzy, but he seemed to have forgotten about it now). 'We can keep *fairly* close to the path, and every now and then, when we see a slab of rock, we'll go off and do a bit of climbing.'

That seemed a good idea to James, and as soon as they'd finished lunch they started. They scrambled about on one or two pretty soft bits until what you'd expect happened—they lost the path. They followed a rabbit-trail—then another—and when that petered out they hadn't enough mountain sense to strike uphill until they found the path again. Instead, they did what mountain lunatics always do, they started to go *down*. They know the world's somewhere below; they want to get back to it; they think that the quickest way is to push downhill.

Well, they hadn't pushed far before they found themselves above the upper slabs of Garnet Fell. They were struggling down through grass and heather—and all of a sudden there they were, with about a hundred and fifty feet of rock below them, not sheer (because rock never is), but sheer enough. A big jump from the top—and you wouldn't strike the face till you were pretty near halfway to the bottom.

Even they could see that wasn't a place to fool about on, and they started to scramble back. Just then, John must have had another of his attacks of mountain sickness; possibly his foot slipped (his shoes were near enough in ribbons); at any rate . . . he fell.

He fell about sixty feet, smashing himself as he hit the rock, and he fetched up on a narrow ledge, p'r'aps fifteen feet long by a couple of feet wide. You'll recognize the place when I tell you it's a climber's disappointment. It's about the best landmark on the face, but you can't get to it. It overhangs, so you can't come up from below, and, above, the rock's like glass. It wasn't absolutely the worse spot he could have chosen, because about ten yards to the west there's a chimney, and the chimney's just possible to a good climber—but the ten yards from the ledge to the chimney are not possible at all. . . .

I suppose John Busson was the first man on that bit of ledge since the beginning of time.

For a minute James didn't realize what had happened. Then he crept to the edge, looked down—and saw his brother lying. 'There was blood coming out of him,' he said.

9

James was a lunatic all right, but he'd got pluck. He didn't go off to find help or look about for some way of getting down—or do any of the things a sane man would have done. He saw his brother down there on the ledge, knew he needed help—and dropped. He lowered his body over the edge, let go with his hands, and fell. Next thing he knew he was beside his brother on the ledge. He doesn't seem to have noticed, at any rate till afterwards, what had happened to himself. He'd cracked two ribs, part of his nose was gone, he'd taken the flesh off his cheeks and forehead, and lost the tips of his fingers where his hands had tried to clutch the rock . . . he was the luckiest fool on earth to get off like that.

He moved along to his brother, and it can't have taken him long to realize the lad was in a bad way. John was lying as no human being ought to lie, and there wasn't a limb or part of a limb that he could move.

James made him as comfortable as he could, put a stone—which was all there was—under his head, and his own coat over his body, and began to tell him he wasn't as bad as all that and they'd be picked up before long. 'Just you keep still, old man,' he said, 'and you'll be as right as rain in no time.'

There was no need to tell John to keep still. It was as much as he could do to raise an eyelid. But he still had the use of his voice, and with that voice he kept saying one word—'*Water*'. If John wants water, thought his brother, he must have some, and he began to look about him.

It was pretty clear there was no water on the ledge; but he remembered having stepped into a little brook not far from where his brother slipped, and he decided to go up and fetch water down from there. The only thing he had to bring it in was his brother's bowler hat, which was still on him when he landed—his own was about a hundred feet below.

He put that hat on his head and began to try and climb straight up the slab. You might as well try to climb Niagara Falls. It was then he noticed what had happened to his fingers, but he seems to have taken it quite coolly, as just something else he'd have to allow for on the climb. He looked round and caught sight of the chimney. 'It was only ten yards away,' he said, 'so I decided to go across.'

How that man made those ten yards—in that condition, in

those clothes, without a rope, or proper boots, or the experience of climbing a back-yard wall—is a mountain mystery. They are impossible, and he did it. That's all there is to say. Having got across, he went up the chimney, reached the spring, bathed his face and hands, and filled the bowler hat. When he got back to the chimney he realized he didn't know how to get the bowler hat down to his brother. But by this time he wouldn't have been stopped by the President of the Alpine Club.

He took off his tie, looped it over his neck, made holes in the hat, knotted the ends of the tie through, and began to go down, with this thing like a beggar's money-box round his neck. He got to the bottom, passed the hat over on to his back, and scrambled across those same ten yards of rock.

I tell you, it makes me ill to think of that journey even for a fit man, who'd lived in mountains all his life. Well, you *can't* think of it, that's all. It isn't near enough possible to think of.

When James got back onto the ledge there was still about an inch and a half of water in the hat, and he poured it into his brother's mouth and down his face. It was dark almost by now, so he must have taken the best part of four hours to do those sixty feet up and down.

How James Busson got through that night, I don't know. Whether he walked up and down; or shouted; or lay still beside his brother; or sang—or stood on his head. He had only his ordinary suit on, and he'd put his coat over his brother. He was in a bad way himself, and he'd no food except some bits of sandwiches, which he reckoned his brother wouldn't want.

In the morning, John was pretty near gone, but not quite—and he still kept saying 'Water'. I suppose because his stomach was mashed-up.

'After a bit, I couldn't stand it any more,' said James. 'I thought I'd go up to the top again and fill the hat.' Fill the hat!—as you or I might talk of filling buckets at a well.

If the journey had been difficult before, it was five times more difficult now. The lad was chilled to the bone. He was hungry, and his wounds were all tender with exposure. He told me he was crying the whole way, but there must have been a bit of something in him, or else the angels bore him up, because he got across those ten yards again and part way up the chimney.

Half up the chimney he felt he couldn't go another inch—and then he had what he thought was a splendid idea. He'd divert the little stream to run down over the rocks towards the ledge, and then he wouldn't have to make that terrible journey every time his brother needed a drink. ('Laying the water on' was what he called it.)

Drawn on by his idea, he got up to the top, worked for a couple of hours, damming and channelling, and at last got the stream to flow the way he wanted. Then he crawled into the chimney, went down, crossed the ten yards for the fourth time—and found his brother had died while he was gone.

The lad seems then to have broken up completely. From that moment he thought of nothing, did nothing, attempted nothing. I don't believe he even shouted—and it was nothing but chance that took us to where he was. 'I put my own coat on again,' he told us. But he didn't take any of his brother's clothes—there was even a broken biscuit in John's pocket which he hadn't touched. And he made no attempt at the climb he'd already done four times. . . .

It was Saturday afternoon when he got back to that ledge, and it was latish Tuesday when we found him, so he was there for three days with the body of his brother. All he had to live on was water—one little trickle of the stream he'd diverted. It ran down to a corner of the ledge; the rest followed a slope in the rock and poured away out of reach. Sometimes it rained. Sometimes it was fine. Every night, at least, it was bitterly cold.

The man who saw him first thought he was gone too. He was leaning back against the rock with his legs dangling over the edge, white as a sheet, except where his face was marked with blood. His damaged hands were laid out on the grass beside him as though they didn't belong.

When we lowered some brandy on a rope and it came down just beside his head, he stared at it—as though either he didn't see it, or it was the most natural thing in the world for brandy to come dangling on ropes over a mountain ledge. He made no sign or movement, and he took no notice when we shouted.

So one of us went down on a rope, made another rope fast round him, and the two came up together—the man who'd gone down trying to keep the lad from getting any more knocks against the rock. Then we went back a second time for the body. We brought the two of them down here, put James to bed, with roaring fires, drink, hot water bottles and God-knows-what—and laid John's body among the bracken in the outhouse.

Two days later James suddenly sat up in bed, called us in, and began to tell us the whole story. He related it all through once, like I've told it you—then he shut up and never said another word about it. He went back to his job, stayed with the same firm all his life, and died, we heard, about five years ago. There was talk at the time of the accident about giving him a medal of some kind, but I don't think it ever came to anything.

Medal or no medal, though, I should say that lad was the finest climber ever came inside this door—James Busson, his name was. You won't find it mentioned in any of the books on mountaineering.

Johnny One-Eye *by Damon Runyon*

This cat I am going to tell you about is a very small cat, and in fact it is only a few weeks old, consequently it is really nothing but an infant cat. To tell the truth, it is just a kitten.

It is grey and white and very dirty and its fur is all frowzled up, so it is a very miserable-looking little kitten to be sure the day it crawls through a broken basement window into an old house in East Fifty-third Street over near Third Avenue in the city of New York and goes from room to room saying merouw, merouw in a low, weak voice until it comes to a room at the head of the stairs on the second storey where a guy by the name of Rudolph is sitting on the floor thinking of not much.

One reason Rudolph is sitting on the floor is because there is nothing else to sit on, as this is an empty house that is all boarded up for years and there is no furniture whatever in it, and another reason is that Rudolph has a .38 slug in his side and really does not feel like doing much of anything but sitting. He is wearing a derby hat and his overcoat, as it is in the wintertime and very cold and he has an automatic Betsy on the floor beside him and naturally he is surprised quite some when the little kitten comes merouwing into the room and he picks up the Betsy and points it at the door in case anyone he does not wish to see is with the kitten. But when he observes that it is all alone, Rudolph puts the Betsy down again and speaks to the kitten as follows:

'Hello, cat,' he says.

Of course the kitten does not say anything in reply except merouw, but it walks right up to Rudolph and climbs on his lap, although the chances are if it knows who Rudolph is it will hightail it out of there quicker than anybody can say scat. There is enough daylight coming through the chinks in the boards over the windows for Rudolph to see that the kitten's right eye is in bad shape, and in fact it is bulged half out of its head in a most distressing manner, and it is plain to be seen that the sight is gone from this eye. It is also plain to be seen that the injury happened recently, and Rudolph gazes at the kitten a while and starts to laugh and says like this:

'Well, cat,' he says, 'you seem to be scuffed up almost as much as I am. We make a fine pair of invalids here together. What is your name, cat?'

Naturally the kitten does not state its name but only goes merouw, and Rudolph says, 'All right, I will call you Johnny. Yes,' he says, 'your tag is now Johnny One-Eye.'

Then he puts the kitten in under his overcoat and pretty soon it gets warm and starts to purr, and Rudolph says: 'Johnny,' he says, 'I will say one thing for you and that is you are plenty game to be able to sing when you are hurt as bad as you are. It is more than I can do.'

But Johnny only goes merouw again and keeps on purring, and by and by it falls sound asleep under Rudolph's coat and Rudolph is wishing the pain in his side will let up long enough for him to do the same.

Well, I suppose you are saying to yourself, what is this Rudolph doing in an old empty house with a slug in his side, so I will explain that the district attorney is responsible for this situation. It seems that the D.A. appears before the grand jury and tells it that Rudolph is an extortion guy and a killer and I do not know what all else, though some of these statements are without doubt a great injustice to Rudolph, as, up to the time the D.A. makes them, Rudolph does not kill anybody of any consequence in years.

In fact, the D.A. claims that Rudolph is nothing but a racket guy and a great knock to the community, and all this upsets Rudolph no little when it comes to his ears in a roundabout way. So he calls up his lawbooks and requests legal advice on the subject, and lawbooks says the best thing he can think of for Rudolph to do is to become as inconspicuous as possible right away, but to please not mention to anyone that he gives this advice.

Lawbooks says he understands the D.A. is requesting indictments and is likely to get them and furthermore, that he is rounding up certain parties that Rudolph is once associated with and trying to get them to remember incidents in Rudolph's early career that may not be entirely to his credit. Lawbooks says he hears that one of these parties is a guy by the name of

Cute Freddy and that Freddy makes a deal with the D.A. to lay off him if he tells everything he knows about Rudolph, so under the circumstances a long journey by Rudolph will be in the interest of everybody concerned.

So Rudolph decides to go on a journey, but then he gets to thinking that maybe Freddy will remember a little matter that Rudolph long since dismisses from his mind and does not wish to have recalled again, which is the time he and Freddy do a job on a guy by the name of Icelander in Troy years ago, and he drops around to Freddy's house to remind him to be sure not to remember this.

But it seems that Freddy mistakes the purpose of Rudolph's visit and starts to out with his rooty-toot-toot, and in order to protect himself it is necessary for Rudolph to take his Betsy and give Freddy a little tattooing. In fact, Rudolph practically crockets his monogram on Freddy's chest and leaves him exceptionally deceased.

But as Rudolph is departing from the neighbourhood, who bobs up but a young guy by the name of Buttsy Fagan, who works for Freddy as a chauffeur and one thing and another, and who is also said to be able to put a slug through a keyhole at forty paces without touching the sides, though I suppose it will have to be a pretty good-sized keyhole. Anyway, he takes a long-distance crack at Rudolph as Rudolph is rounding a corner, but all Buttsy can see of Rudolph at the moment is a little piece of his left side, and this is what Buttsy hits, although no-one knows it at the time, except of course Rudolph, who just keeps on departing.

Now this incident causes quite a stir in police circles, and the D.A. is very indignant over losing a valuable witness, and when they are unable to locate Rudolph at once, a reward of five thousand dollars is offered for information leading to his capture alive or dead, and some think they really mean dead. Indeed, it is publicly stated that it is not a good idea for anyone to take any chances with Rudolph, as he is known to be armed and is such a character as will be sure to resent being captured, but they do not explain that this is only because Rudolph knows the D.A. wishes to place him in the old rocking chair at Sing Sing and that Rudolph is quite allergic to the idea.

Anyway, the cops go looking for Rudolph in Hot Springs and Miami and every other place except where he is, which is right in New York, wandering around town with the slug in his side, knocking at the doors of old friends requesting assistance. But all the old friends do for him is to slam the doors in his face and forget they ever see him, as the D.A. is very tough on parties who assist guys he is looking for, claiming that this is something most illegal called harbouring fugitives.

He cannot even consult a doctor about the slug in his side, as he knows that nowadays the first thing a doctor will do about a guy with a gunshot wound is to report him to the cops. So he just does the best he can about the slug and goes wandering here and there and around and about, and the blats keep printing his picture and saying, where is Rudolph?

Where he is some of the time is in Central Park trying to get some sleep, but of course even the blats will consider it foolish to go looking for Rudolph there in such cold weather, as he is known as a guy who enjoys his comfort at all times. In fact, it is comfort that Rudolph misses more than anything, as the slug is commencing to cause him great pain, and naturally the pain turns Rudolph's thoughts to the author of same, and he remembers that he once hears somebody say that Buttsy lives over in East Fifty-third Street.

So one night Rudolph decides to look up Buttsy and cause him a little pain in return, and he is moseying through Fifty-third when he gets so weak he falls down on the sidewalk in front of the old house and rolls down a short flight of steps that lead from the street level to a little railed-in area-way and ground floor or basement door, and before he stops rolling he brings up against the door itself, and it creaks open inward as he bumps it. After he lays there awhile Rudolph can see that the house is empty, and he crawls on inside.

Then, when he feels stronger, Rudolph makes his way upstairs because the basement is damp and mice keep trotting back and forth over him, and eventually he winds up in the room where Johnny One-Eye finds him the following afternoon, and the reason Rudolph settles down in this room is because it commands the stairs. Naturally, this is important to a guy in Rudolph's situation, though after he is sitting there for about fourteen hours before Johnny comes along he can see that he is not going to be much disturbed by traffic. But he considers it a very fine place, indeed, to remain planted until he is able to resume his search for Buttsy.

Well, after a while Johnny One-Eye wakes up and comes from under the coat and looks at Rudolph out of his good eye, and Rudolph waggles his fingers and Johnny plays with them, catching one finger in his front paws and biting it gently, and this pleases Rudolph no little, as he never before has any personal experience with a kitten. However, he remembers observing one when he is a boy down in Houston Street, so he takes a piece of paper out of his pocket and makes a little ball of it and rolls it along the floor, and Johnny bounces after it very lively indeed. But Rudolph can see that the bad eye is getting worse, and finally he says to Johnny like this:

'Johnny,' he says, 'I guess you must be suffering more than I am. I remember there are some pet shops over on Lexington Avenue not far from here, and when it gets good and dark I am going to take you out and see if we can find a cat croaker to do something about your eye. Yes, Johnny,' Rudolph says, 'I will also get something for you to eat. You must be starved.'

Johnny One-Eye says merouw to this and keeps on playing with the paper ball, but soon it comes on dark outside and inside, too, and in fact, it is so dark inside that Rudolph cannot see his hand before him. Then he puts his Betsy in a side pocket of his overcoat and picks up Johnny and goes downstairs, feeling his way in the dark and easing along a step at a time until he gets to the basement door. Naturally, Rudolph does not wish to strike any matches, because he is afraid someone outside may see the light and get nosey.

By moving very slowly, Rudolph finally gets to Lexington Avenue, and while he is going along he remembers the time he walks from 125th Street in Harlem down to 110th with six slugs in him and never feels as bad as he does now. He gets to thinking that maybe he is not the guy he used to be, which of course is very true, as Rudolph is now forty-odd years of age and is fat around the middle and getting bald, and he also does some thinking about what a pleasure it will be to him to find this Buttsy and cause him the pain he is personally suffering.

There are not many people in the streets, and those that

are go hurrying along because it is so cold, and none of them pay any attention to Rudolph or Johnny One-Eye either, even though Rudolph staggers a little now and then like a guy who is rummed up, although of course it is only weakness. The chances are he is also getting a little feverish and light-headed, because finally he stops a cop who is going along swinging his arms to keep warm and ask him if he knows where there is a pet shop, and it is really most indiscreet of such a guy as Rudolph to be interviewing cops. But the cop just points up the street and goes on without looking twice at Rudolph, and Rudolph laughs and pokes Johnny with a finger and says:

'No, Johnny One-Eye,' he says, 'the cop is not a dope for not recognizing Rudolph. Who can figure the hottest guy in forty-eight states to be going along a street with a little cat in his arms? Can you, Johnny?'

Johnny says merouw, and pretty soon Rudolph comes to the pet shop the cop points out. Rudolph goes inside and says to the guy like this:

'Are you a cat croaker?' Rudolph says. 'Do you know what to do about a little cat that has a hurt eye?'

'I am a kind of a vet,' the guy said.

'Then take a glaum at Johnny One-Eye and see what you can do for him,' Rudolph says.

Then he hands Johnny over to the guy, and the guy looks at Johnny a while and says:

'Mister,' he says, 'the best thing I can do for this cat is to put it out of its misery. You better let me give it something right now. It will just go to sleep and never know what happens.'

Well, at this, Rudolph grabs Johnny One-Eye out of the guy's hands and puts him under his coat and drops a duke on the Betsy in his pocket as if he is afraid the guy will take Johnny away from him again, and he says to the guy like this:

'No, no, no,' Rudolph says. 'I cannot bear to think of such a thing. What about some kind of an operation? I remember they take a bum lamp out of Joe the Goat at Bellevue one time, and he is O.K. now.'

'Nothing will do your cat any good,' the guy says. 'It is a goner. It will start having fits pretty soon and die sure. What is the idea of trying to save such a cat as this? It is no kind of a cat to begin with. It is just a cat. You can get a million like it for a nickel.'

'No,' Rudolph says, 'This is not just a cat. This is Johnny One-Eye. He is my only friend in the world. He is the only living thing that ever comes pushing up against me warm and friendly and trust me in my whole life. I feel sorry for him.'

'I feel sorry for him, too,' the guy says. 'I always feel sorry for animals that get hurt, and for people.'

'I do not feel sorry for people,' Rudolph says, 'I only feel sorry for Johnny One-Eye. Give me some kind of stuff that Johnny will eat.'

'Your cat wants milk,' the guy says. 'You can get some at the delicatessen store down at the corner. Mister,' he says, 'you look sick yourself. Can I do anything for you?'

But Rudolph only shakes his head and goes on out and down to the delicatessen joint, where he buys a bottle of milk, and this transaction reminds him that he is very short in the moo department. In fact, he can only find a five-dollar note in his pockets, and he remembers that he has no way of getting any more when this runs out, which is a very sad predicament indeed for a guy who is accustomed to plenty of moo at all times.

Then Rudolph returns to the old house and sits down on the floor again and gives Johnny One-Eye some of the milk in his derby hat, as he neglects buying something for Johnny to drink out of. But Johnny offers no complaint. He laps up the milk and curls himself into a wad in Rudolph's lap and purrs.

Rudolph takes a swig of the milk himself, but it makes him sick, for by this time Rudolph is really far from being in the pink of condition. He not only has the pain in his side but he has a heavy cold, which he probably catches from lying on the basement floor or maybe sleeping in the park, and he is wheezing no little. He commences to worry that he may get too ill to continue looking for Buttsy, as he can see that if it is not for Buttsy he will not be in this situation, suffering the way he is, but on a long journey to some place.

He takes to going off into long stretches of a kind of stupor, and every time he comes out of one of these stupors the first thing he does is to look around for Johnny One-Eye, and Johnny is always right there either playing with the paper ball or purring in Rudolph's lap. He is a great comfort to Rudolph, but after a while Rudolph notices that Johnny seems to be running out of zip, and he also notices that he is running out of zip himself, especially when he discovers that he is no longer able to get to his feet.

It is along in the late afternoon of the day following the night Rudolph goes out of the house that he hears someone coming up the stairs, and naturally he picks up his Betsy and gets ready for action, when he also hears a very small voice calling kitty, kitty, kitty, and he realizes that the party that is coming can be nobody but a child. In fact, a minute later a little pretty of maybe six years of age comes into the room all out of breath and says to Rudolph like this:

'How do you do?' she says. 'Have you seen my kitty?'

Then she spots Johnny One-Eye in Rudolph's lap and runs over and sits down beside Rudolph and takes Johnny in her arms, and at first Rudolph is inclined to resent this and has a notion to give her a good boffing, but he is too weak to exert himself in such a manner.

'Who are you?' Rudolph says to the little pretty, 'and,' he says, 'where do you live and how do you get in this house?'

'Why,' she says, 'I am Elsie, and I live down the street, and I am looking everywhere for my kitty for three days, and the door is open downstairs and I know kitty likes to go in doors that are open, so I came to find her, and here she is.'

'I guess I forgot to close it last night,' Rudolph says. 'I seem to be very forgetful lately.'

'What is your name?' Elsie asks, 'and why are you sitting on the floor in the cold and where are all your chairs? Do you have any little girls like me and do you love them dearly?'

'No,' Rudolph says, 'by no means and not at all.'

'Well,' Elsie says, 'I think you are a nice man for taking care of my kitty. Do you love kitty?'

'Look,' Rudolph says, 'his name is not kitty. His name is Johnny One-Eye, because he has only one eye.'

'I call her kitty,' Elsie says. 'But,' she says, 'Johnny One-Eye is a nice name too, and if you like it best I will call her Johnny and I will leave her here with you to take care of always and I will come to see her every day. You see,' she says, 'if I take Johnny home Buttsy will only kick her again.'

'Buttsy?' Rudolph says. 'Do I hear you say Buttsy? Is his other name Fagan?'

'Why, yes,' Elsie says. 'Do you know him?'

'No,' Rudolph says, 'but I hear of him. What is he to you?'

'He is my new daddy,' Elsie says. 'My other one and my best one is dead, and so mamma makes Buttsy my new one. He is very mean. He kicks Johnny and hurts her eye and makes her run away. He kicks my mamma too. Buttsy kicks everybody and everything when he is mad, and he is always mad.'

'He is a louse to kick a little cat,' Rudolph says.

'Yes,' Elsie says, 'that is what Mr O'Toole says he is for kicking my mamma, but my mamma says it is not a nice word.'

'Who is Mr O'Toole?' Rudolph says.

'He is the policeman,' Elsie says. 'He lives across the street from us, and he is very nice to me. Now I must go home,' Elsie says, 'because this is a night Buttsy comes in for his supper, and I have to be in bed before he gets there so I will not bother him. Buttsy does not like little girls. Buttsy does not like little kittens, Buttsy does not like little anythings. My mamma is afraid of Buttsy, and so am I. But,' she says, 'I will leave Johnny here with you and come back tomorrow to see her.'

'Listen, Elsie,' Rudolph says, 'does Mr O'Toole come home tonight to his house for his supper, too?'

'Oh, yes,' Elsie says. 'He comes home every night. Sometimes when there is a night Buttsy is not coming in for his supper my mamma lets me go over to Mr O'Toole's and I play with his dog Charley, but you must never tell Buttsy this, because he does not like Mr O'Toole either. But this is a night Buttsy is coming, and that is why my mamma tells me to get in early.'

Now Rudolph takes an old letter out of his inside pocket and a pencil out of another pocket, and he scribbles a few lines on the envelope and stretches himself out on the floor and begins groaning, oh, oh, oh, and then he says to Elsie like this:

'Look, Elsie,' he says, 'you are a smart little kid and you pay strict attention to what I am going to say to you. Do not go to bed tonight until Buttsy gets in. Then,' Rudolph says, 'you tell him you come in this old house looking for your cat and that you hear somebody groaning like I do just now in the room at the head of the stairs and that you find a guy who says his name is Rudolph lying on the floor so sick he cannot move. Tell him the front door of the basement is open. But,' Rudolph says, 'you must not tell him that Rudolph tells you to say these things. Do you understand?'

'Oh,' Elsie says, 'do you want him to come here? He will kick Johnny again if he does.'

'He will come here, but he will not kick Johnny,' Rudolph says. 'He will come here, or I am the worst guesser in the world. Tell him what I look like, Elsie. Maybe he will ask you if you see a gun. Tell him you do not see one. You do not see a gun, do you, Elsie?'

'No,' Elsie says, 'only the one in your hand when I come in, but you put it under your coat. Buttsy has a gun and Mr O'Toole has a gun, but Buttsy says I am never, never to tell anybody about his or he will kick me the way he does my mamma.'

'Well,' Rudolph says, 'you must not remember seeing mine, either. Now,' he says, 'if Buttsy leaves the house to come and see me, as I am pretty sure he will, you run over to Mr O'Toole's house and give him this note, but do not tell Buttsy or your mamma either about the note. If Buttsy does not leave, it is my hard luck, but you give the note to Mr O'Toole, anyway. Now tell me what you are to do, Elsie,' Rudolph says, 'so I can see if you have got everything correct.'

'I am to go on home and wait for Buttsy,' she says, 'and I am to tell him Rudolph is lying on the floor of this dirty old house with a fat stomach and a big nose making noises and that he is very sick and the basement door is open and there is no gun if he asks me, and when Buttsy comes to see you I am to take this note to Mr O'Toole, but Buttsy and my mamma are not to know I have the note, and if Buttsy does not leave I am to give it to Mr O'Toole anyway and you are to stay here and take care of Johnny my kitten.'

'That is swell,' Rudolph says, 'Now you run along.'

So Elsie leaves, and Rudolph sits up again against the wall, because his side feels easier this way and Johnny One-Eye is in his lap purring very low and the dark comes on until it is blacker inside the room than in the middle of a tunnel, and Rudolph feels that he is going into another stupor and he has a tough time fighting it off.

Afterwards some of the neighbours claim they remember

hearing a shot inside the house and then two more in quick succession and then all is quiet until a little later when Officer O'Toole and half a dozen other cops and an ambulance with a doctor come busting into the street and swarm into the joint with their guns out and their flash-lights going. The first thing they find is Buttsy at the foot of the stairs with two bullet wounds close together in his throat, and naturally, he is real dead.

Rudolph is still sitting against the wall with what seems to be a small bundle of fur in his lap, but which turns out to be what is left of this little cat I am telling you about, although nobody pays any attention to it at first. They are more interested in getting the come-alongs on Rudolph's wrists, but before they move him he pulls his clothes aside and shows the doctor where the slug is in his side, and the doctor takes one glaum and shakes his head and says:

'Gangrene,' he says. 'I think you have pneumonia, too, from the way you are blowing.'

'I know,' Rudolph says. 'I knew this morning. Not much chance, hey, croaker?'

'Not much,' the doctor says.

'Well, cops,' Rudolph says, 'load me in. I do not suppose you want Johnny, seeing that he is dead.'

'Johnny who?' one of the cops says.

'Johnny One-Eye,' Rudolph says. 'This little cat here in my lap. Buttsy shoots Johnny's only good eye out and takes most of his noddle with it. I never see a more wonderful shot. Well, Johnny is better off, but I feel sorry about him, as he is my best friend down to the last.'

Then he begins to laugh, and the cop asks him what tickles him so much, and Rudolph says:

'Oh,' he says, 'I am thinking of the joke on Buttsy. I am positive he will come looking for me, all right, not only because of the little altercation between Cute Freddy and me but because the chances are Buttsy is greatly embarrassed by not tilting me over the first time, as of course he never knows he wings me. Furthermore,' Rudolph says, 'and this is the best reason of all, Buttsy will realize that if I am in his neighbourhood it is by no means a good sign for him, even if he hears I am sick.'

'Well,' Rudolph says, 'I figure that with any kind of a

square rattle I will have a better chance of nailing him than he has of nailing me, but that even if he happens to nail me, O'Toole will get my note in time to arrive here and nab Buttsy on the spot with his gun on him. And,' Rudolph says, 'I know it will be a great pleasure to the D.A. to settle Buttsy for having a gun on him.'

'But,' Rudolph says, 'as soon as I hear Buttsy coming on the sneaksby up the stairs, I can see I am taking all the worst of it because I am now wheezing like a busted valve and you can hear me a block away except when I hold my breath, which is very difficult indeed, considering the way I am already greatly tuckered out. No,' Rudolph says, 'it does not look any too good for me as Buttsy keeps coming up the stairs, as I can tell he is doing by a little faint creak in the boards now and then. I am in no shape to manoeuvre round the room, and pretty soon he will be on the landing, and then all he will have to do is to wait there until he hears me, which he is bound to do unless I stop breathing altogether. Naturally,' Rudolph says, 'I do not care to risk a blast in the dark without knowing where he is, as something tells me Buttsy is not a guy you can miss in safety.'

'Well,' Rudolph says, 'I notice several times before this that in the dark Johnny One-Eye's good glim shines like a big spark, so when I feel Buttsy is about to hit the landing, although of course I cannot see him, I flip Johnny's ball of paper across the room to the wall just opposite the door, and tough as he must be feeling, Johnny chases after it when he hears it light. I figure Buttsy will hear Johnny playing with the paper and see his eye shining and think it is me and take a pop at it and that his gun flash will give me a crack at him.'

'It all works out just like I dope it,' Rudolph says, 'but,' he says, 'I never give Buttsy credit for being such a marksman as to be able to hit a cat's eye in the dark. If I know this I will never stick Johnny out in front the way I do. It is a good thing I never give Buttsy a second shot. He is a lily. Yes,' Rudolph says, 'I can remember when I can use a guy like him.'

'Buttsy is no account,' the cop says. 'He is a good riddance. He is the makings of a worse guy than you.'

'Well,' Rudolph says, 'it is a good lesson to him for kicking a little cat.'

Then they take Rudolph to a hospital, and this is where I see him and piece out this story of Johnny One-Eye, and Officer O'Toole is at Rudolph's bedside keeping guard over him, and I remember that not long before Rudolph chalks out he looks at O'Toole and says to him like this:

'Copper,' he says, 'there is no chance of them out-juggling the kid on the reward moo, is there?'

'No,' O'Toole says, 'no chance. I keep the note you send me by Elsie saying she will tell me where you are. It is information leading to your capture just as the reward offer states. Rudolph,' he says, 'it is a nice thing you do for Elsie and her mother, although,' he says, 'it is not nearly as nice as icing Buttsy for them.'

'By the way, copper,' Rudolph says, 'there is the remainders of a pound note in my pants pocket when I am brought here. I want you to do me a favour. Get it from the desk and buy Elsie another cat and name it Johnny, will you?'

'Sure,' O'Toole says. 'Anything else?'

'Yes,' Rudolph says, 'be sure it has two good eyes.'

Playing with Fire *by D J Brindley*

Some schools breed optimism; others despair. I taught in a happy school where people were filled with enthusiasm, and I also taught in a school where resentment and discord prevailed. Fights would occur there almost daily and bullying was rife, not least of students by staff. The Headmaster was something of an ogre: pompous, authoritarian, and fearful of losing his public image.

When I arrived he had just expelled one boy for distributing a notorious international newspaper. A month later he expelled another for wearing grey trousers to school instead of the regulation charcoal. Then another boy ran away from both home and school on account of his intimidatory attitude concerning some petty offence.

The students in this sort of atmosphere were either sullen and unresponsive or rebellious to the point of violence. Two boys who felt particularly bitter were Saville and Jones. They belonged to a Fifth Form class that had been written off as irresponsible trouble-makers virtually from their inception in the school. In fact they proved to be very delightful characters: effervescent and full of nonsense, though devastatingly loyal once their sympathies had been engaged. But the Head's main aim was to get rid of them as soon as he could.

I was taking them through *Macbeth* one day, (a somewhat irrelevant preparation for the lives of adolescent boys ostensibly interested in only the three S's: soccer, smoking, and sex), when Saville suddenly stood up from his desk near the door and switched off the electric light. Then he sat down, peered into his book, realised he could see nothing, so quickly stood up and switched it back on. A few moments later he started again: Off—On, Off—On, jumping up and down like a demented yo-yo. I thought it best to ignore the first interruption, but after the second remarked sardonically: 'We must thank Saville. He is obviously sensitive to the fact that *Macbeth* is a play of light and darkness in which the light of life is suddenly extinguished by the bloody hand of a murderer.' But Saville had clearly been driven to this rather feeble display of self-expression by tensions of which I was unaware.

On another occasion I noticed him conferring clandestinely with Jones, who usually sat silent beneath steel spectacles and an oppressive weight of dark hair. There was an air of suppressed devilry about Saville and clownish expectancy in the class. I played ignorant. Jones was taking something from his pocket: a cigarette-lighter. Saville had a little heap of paper on the desk behind his book. Suddenly he looked round, smiled with disarming innocence, then set fire to the paper. It flared up brightly and smoke rose into the air.

'Put out your fire, Saville,' I said, affecting a coolness I didn't feel.

'Can't sir, it isn't finished.' The smell of smoke began to fill the classroom.

'What are you burning?' I had to restrain my annoyance.

'Science notes, sir. Mr Wilkins says I'm going to fail.'

'Get rid of that mess and see me after the lesson.'

'Very good, sir.' He used the back of his English book to shovel the burning paper into the waste-paper basket, then ceremoniously stamped out the remains.

'And use your cigarette-lighter for the right purpose in future, Jones.'

'He smokes twenty a day, sir,'—this from one of the heaviest smokers.

'And I suppose you only chew bubble-gum, Spears?'

'No, sir. Mam says it's not good for the teeth.'

'Nor for your fingers by the look of them—now shut up and get on with the lesson,'—as he opened his mouth for a further rejoinder.

I threatened them with death if they didn't pass English. In the trial exam Saville scored 77%, just missing a Distinction. In Science he got 8 for Physics and 3 for Chemistry.

I never had any more trouble from either of them, but a few weeks after the incident their hormones started getting lively again and they played two practical jokes which had really serious consequences.

Decorating the school's walls at tempting places were a number of fire hoses. These were set for automatic release so that as soon as they were plucked from the wall water would spray out. Being fairly new, their efficacy had not been generally proved, so Saville conspired with Jones to carry out a simple test.

It was a lunch-hour lull when prefects were less vigilant than usual. Jones had signalled that the corridor was clear and Saville with a quick movement yanked the hose-arm from its place. The result exceeded their wildest expectations. The hose twisted in Saville's hands and water shot forth into the air, splattering ceiling, walls and floor, and drenching the trousers of an incredulous junior standing nearby. If they'd kept their heads all might have been well; instead they dropped the hose and water sprayed freely in all directions. In a panic they ran down the staircase and out of the building while the volume of water grew and came cascading down the steps. Boys collected, masters came out to see what was happening, and prefects ran about shouting angry orders to add to the general confusion. It took two caretakers an evening's work to clean up the mess.

They were suspended from school for four weeks. Then the telephone calls started. For though Saville and Jones had more or less worked off their hatreds, the remainder of the Fifth Form hadn't. Unfortunately the two of them became implicated.

It began with a Danish book, 'How to Undermine your Teacher's Confidence', which described effective methods of student revenge against pedagogical tyranny. If your teacher set you too much homework you were advised to ring him at midnight after he'd gone to bed and ask him if you ought to continue working as his assignment was still not finished. Then if he wanted you to carry on you were to ring him again at 3 a.m. and ask for advice on a particular problem that had stumped you for the last hour. Under the pressure of prolonged psychological warfare the teacher's nerves might eventually give way.

The Fifth Form were employing a modified version of this when Saville and Jones were away on their Siberian holiday. The conversation would go something like:

'Hello. Is that Mr Jaggers?'

'Speaking.'

(Smooth voice) 'Oh. Chief Education Officer here. I hear

you've been having trouble with your students at Pilsdown Crammer School?'

'I don't quite understand.'

'I understand the pupils have been complaining about your attitude, Mr Jaggers.'

'I don't follow.'

(Not so smooth) 'No. Apparently not. Well look here, Jaggers. We hate your blasted guts and the sooner you leave the bloody place, the better.'

They continued phoning undetected for a month. Now while Saville and Jones were away they had only heard about the calls. When they returned they were persuaded to listen in along with six others sardined in a telephone booth. And they were seen.

The next day they were ruthlessly cross-questioned for an hour during which the Head's anger steadily rose.

'I know you were there!' he shouted. 'Don't try to deceive me, you lying louts.' He pointed at Saville. 'You are the ring-leader. I recognised your voice all along.' His imagination grew. 'How dare you sabotage the good discipline of my school?' Saville consistently denied being the ringleader and Jones supported him. But to no avail. The Head needed a load-horse to carry the blame and he treated their denials with contempt. They were expelled on the following day—six weeks before their final exams.

When I walked out of the staffroom that afternoon they had just heard the verdict. Fear and unbelief were written large across their faces.

'He's kicked us out, sir!'

'We did nothing!'

'He didn't even listen to what we said.'

'He had no proof.'

'Called us ringleaders. Swore we'd organised the whole thing.'

'Did you?'

'No sir. Honest. We were just listening in and laughing.'

'What are you going to do?'

'Don't know. My Dad'll kill me when he hears.' (Jones)

'Six weeks to go to the exams. (Saville) Then we'd've left the damn place anyway.'

'It was only a joke, sir. Anyway, they deserved all they got.' (The masters)

'Same as the fire-hose, sir. Everybody plays jokes. Oh God, here's Creamy.' (A teacher)

'My Dad'll kill me.'

'Here. Lend me your book. This is our address. Try to come round if you can. We'll talk about it later.' Then they were crowded outside like pathetic sheep not knowing where to go.

The phone rang at 9.0 p.m. that evening. It was Saville. He sounded desperate.

'I'm down at the beach, sir, at Southgate. I've run away from home.'

'Who's with you?'

'No-one. I came by bike. I think the police are after me.'

'Hold on. How far is it? I'll come down. Where will you be?'

'In the bus shelter. Do you think I ought to go farther away?'

'No. Just wait. We'll be there in half-an-hour. We'll see you at the Pavilion. O.K.?'

I turned to my wife.

'It's Saville. He's run away. In this mood he could do anything. He says the police are looking for him.'

In ten minutes we were on the road in driving rain. My wife with her usual practicality had filled a bag full of chicken sandwiches, raw carrots, fruit and chocolate, and wrapped an extra pullover around it all.

'It'll be freezing down there at night. My God—he wouldn't commit suicide, would he? Do you think he's a bit unbalanced?'

All I knew of Saville came from his essays which described his early life, first in the Gorbals, the slum area of Glasgow, then in the outskirts of London where he'd seen flick-knife fights and taken part in schoolboy raids on sweet-stores when he was twelve. Yet despite his tough exterior I believed he was desperately insecure within himself. Even his manner of speaking was staccato and over-rapid. Impulsiveness had characterised nearly all his behaviour, from the light-switch and the hose to this latest animal-like flight.

'He should be all right. We must just let him talk it out.'

The sea was pounding when we arrived and the skies were black with rain. We found him in the deserted Amusement

Arcade staring at the pinball machines, now dead as coffins.

'The police have been around,' he jerked out. 'My parents must have phoned them.'

'What are you going to do?' I asked for the second time that day.

'I've got to stay out. Expose the Bull. (The Head) Show him up.'

'How do you mean?'

'He's afraid of one thing: his public image. If the papers get onto this there's sure to be a story. There's also that other guy who's run away from school. They haven't caught him yet. When they find out that two of us are missing there'll be a hell of a row. Then someone might catch on that there's something wrong at Paradise Place.'

So that was his idea. I flashed a grin at my wife.

'Where are you going to sleep, John?' she asked.

'No idea. I thought maybe of a hotel.'

'Not a chance. They're sure to ask questions. What about—'

'Look out, the cops!'

We moved back into the darkness of the Arcade as two police-vans came rumbling by like tanks. Their lights disappeared up the hill and we breathed heavily.

'Could he stay at our house, darling?' My wife's ingenuity at work.

'You're crazy! What if they found out? We'd get sacked on the spot.' (Not that I should have wept tears of regret.)

'Well how about the ruin?'

We set off as yet another police patrol came by, headlights probing. A few miles away was an accessible fortress, suitable for concealment but hardly a congenial guest house. As we climbed out of the car the keep rose up solitary and forbidding, and cloud-wisps were threading their way through the gaunt arrow-gaps in the battlements. Rain was blowing in our faces.

'Mm. I'm not so sure there'll be any place there—' Poor Saville. He looked to my wife for reassurance.

'Wait. You remember our walk along the beach? What about the gun-shelter? They wouldn't think of looking for him there.'

The rain had eased a little as we stepped out onto the beach, but the waves were rolling and high.

'It's round the headland,' I explained, 'it's an old stone turret only about eight feet high, but there's room to lie down inside and no chance of being seen. Wait here and I'll see if there's a way round.'

I cut across the rocks and was soon lost in the mist. The tide was in and I found myself knee-deep in water. I tried to climb the cliff but it was too steep. A lump of rock came away in my hand and then there was nothing but rock and water up to the waist. I sploshed back.

My wife had been talking loudly to appear confident, inwardly aware only of the crashing sound of the tide and my increasing absence.

'No go. It's too deep.' I was soaked to the skin. Saville suddenly pointed.

'What's that behind the trees?'

There was a thicket standing back from the beach with a now definable outline in its midst. Another shelter. I scrambled forward and disappeared again.

'It's fine. There's a concrete ledge inside for you to sleep on. Here, take this stick in case of rats.'

'And there's some food and a spare jersey.'

'Can you ring us tomorrow to let us know how things are?'

We slept little that night, imagining all possible kinds of misfortune, but Saville—so he told us—slept well. He had the courage to stay out another two nights in the gun-shelter and only returned home five days later, by which time the press had got hold of the story, there were rumours of ill-treatment at the school, and several irate parents had been on the phone to the Headmaster.

When the exams came Saville passed everything except Science. Jones was less lucky, failing five out of seven. Of the two he seemed to suffer the more. He tried to get employment but was refused on account of a damning testimonial the Head wrote for him. But after a few months without work both boys managed to get fairly good jobs. Saville is now working for an electrical firm and Jones is a clerk at the Fire Station.

Tony Kytes *by Thomas Hardy*

I shall never forget Tony's face. 'Twas a little, round, firm, tight face, with a seam here and there left by the smallpox, but not enough to hurt his looks in a woman's eye, though he'd had it baddish when he was a boy. So very serious-looking and unsmiling 'a was, that young man, that it really seemed as if he couldn't laugh at all without great pain to his conscience. He looked very hard at a small speck in your eye when talking to 'ee. And there was no more sign of a whisker or beard on Tony Kytes' face than on the palm of my hand. He used to sing 'The Tailor's Breeches' with a religious manner, as if it were a hymn:

'O the petticoats went off, and the breeches they went on!' and all the rest of the scandalous stuff. He was quite the women's favourite, and in return for their likings he loved 'em in shoals.

But in course of time Tony got fixed down to one in particular Milly Richards, a nice, light, small, tender little thing; and it was soon said that they were engaged to be married. One Saturday he had been to market to do business for his father, and was driving home the waggon in the afternoon. When he reached the foot of the very hill we shall be going over in ten minutes who should he see waiting for him at the top but Unity Sallet, a handsome girl, one of the young women he'd been very tender toward before he'd got engaged to Milly.

As soon as Tony came up to her she said, 'My dear Tony, will you give me a lift home?'

'That I will, darling,' said Tony. 'You don't suppose I could refuse 'ee?'

She smiled a smile, and up she hopped, and on drove Tony.

'Tony,' she says, in a sort of tender chide, 'why did ye desert me for that other one? In what is she better than I? I should have made 'ee a finer wife, and a more loving one too. 'Tisn't girls that are so easily won at first that are the best. Think how long we've known each other—ever since we were children almost—now haven't we, Tony?'

'Yes, that we have,' says Tony, a-struck with the truth o't.

'And you've never seen anything in me to complain of, have ye, Tony? Now tell the truth to me?'

'I never have, upon my life,' says Tony.

'And—can you say I'm not pretty, Tony? Now look at me!'

He let his eyes light upon her for a long while. 'I really can't,' says he. 'In fact, I never knowed you was so pretty before!'

'Prettier than she?'

What Tony would have said to that nobody knows, for before he could speak, what should he see ahead, over the hedge past the turning, but a feather he knew well—the feather in Milly's hat—she to whom he had been thinking of putting the question as to giving out the banns that very week.

'Unity,' says he, as mild as he could, 'here's Milly coming. Now I shall catch it mightily if she see 'ee riding here with me; and if you get down she'll be turning the corner in a moment, and, seeing 'ee in the road, she'll know we've been coming on together. Now, dearest Unity, will ye, to avoid all unpleasantness, which I know ye can't bear any more than I, will ye lie down in the back part of the waggon, and let me cover you over with the tarpaulin till Milly has passed? It will all be done in a minute. Do!—and I'll think over what we've said; and perhaps I shall put a loving question to you after all, instead of to Milly. 'Tisn't true that it is all settled between her and me.'

Well, Unity Sallet agreed, and lay down at the back of the waggon, and Tony covered her over, so that the waggon seemed to be empty but for the loose tarpaulin; and then he drove on to meet Milly.

'My dear Tony!' cries Milly, looking up with a little pout at him as he came near. 'How long you've been coming home! Just as if I didn't live at Upper Longpuddle at all! And I've come to meet you as you asked me to do, and to ride back with you, and talk over our future home—since you asked me, and I promised. But I shouldn't have come else, Mr Tony!'

'Ay, my dear, I did ask 'ee—to be sure I did, now I think of it—but I had quite forgot it. To ride back with me, did you say, dear Milly?'

'Well, of course! What can I do else? Surely you don't want me to walk, now I've come all this way?'

'O no, no! I was thinking you might be going on to town to meet your mother. I saw her there—and she looked as if she might be expecting 'ee.'

'O no; she's just home. She came across the fields, and so got back before you.'

'Ah! I didn't know that,' says Tony. And there was no help for it but to take her up beside him.

They talked on very pleasantly, and looked at the trees, and beasts, and birds, and insects, and at the ploughman at work in the fields, till presently who should they see looking out of the upper window of a house that stood beside the road they were following, but Hannah Jolliver, another young beauty of the place at that time, and the very first woman that Tony had fallen in love with—before Milly and before Unity, in fact— the one that he had almost arranged to marry instead of Milly. She was a much more dashing girl than Milly Richards, though he'd not thought much of her of late. The house Hannah was looking from was her aunt's.

'My dear Milly—my coming wife, as I may call 'ee,' says Tony in his modest way, and not so loud that Unity could overhear, 'I see a young woman a-looking out of the window, who I think may accost me. The fact is, Milly, she had a notion that I was wishing to marry her, and since she's discovered I've promised another, and a prettier than she, I'm rather afeared of her temper if she sees us together. Now, Milly, would you do me a favour—my coming wife, as I may say?'

'Certainly, dearest Tony,' says she.

'Then would ye creep under the empty sacks just here in the front of the waggon, and hide there out of sight till we've passed the house? She hasn't seen us yet. You see, we ought to live in peace and goodwill since 'tis almost Christmas, and 'twill prevent angry passions rising, which we always should do.'

'I don't mind, to oblige you, Tony,' Milly said; and though she didn't care much about doing it, she crept under, and crouched down just behind the seat, Unity being snug at the other end. So they drove on till they got near the roadside cottage. Hannah had soon seen him coming, and waited at the window, looking down upon him. She tossed her head a little disdainfully and smiled off-hand.

'Well, aren't you going to be civil enough to ask me to ride home with you!' she says, seeing that he was for driving past with a nod and a smile.

'Ah, to be sure! What was I thinking of?' said Tony, in a flutter. 'But you seem as if you was staying at your aunt's?'

'No, I am not,' she said. 'Don't you see I have my bonnet and jacket on? I have only called to see her on my way home. How can you be so stupid, Tony?'

'In that case—ah—of course you must come along wi' me,' says Tony, feeling a dim sort of sweat rising up inside his clothes. And he reined in the horse, and waited till she'd come downstairs, and then helped her up beside him, her feet outside. He drove on again, his face as long as a face that was a round one by nature well could be.

Hannah looked round sideways into his eyes. 'This is nice, isn't it, Tony?' she said. 'I like riding with you.'

Tony looked back into her eyes. 'And I with you,' he said after a while. In short, having considered her, he warmed up, and the more he looked at her the more he liked her, till he couldn't for the life of him think why he had ever said a word about marriage to Milly or Unity while Hannah Jolliver was in question. So they sat a little closer and closer, their feet upon the foot-board and their shoulders touching, and Tony thought over and over again how handsome Hannah was. He spoke tenderer and tenderer, and called her 'dear Hannah' in a whisper at last.

'You've settled it with Milly by this time, I suppose,' she said.

'No-no, not exactly.'

'What? How low you talk, Tony.'

'Yes—I've a kind of hoarseness. I said, not exactly.'

'I suppose you mean to?'

'Well, as to that—' His eyes rested on her face, and hers on his. He wondered how he could have been such a fool as not to follow up Hannah. 'My sweet Hannah!' he burst out, taking her hand, not being really able to help it, and forgetting Milly and Unity, and all the world besides. 'Settled it? I don't think I have.'

'Hark!' says Hannah.

'What?' says Tony, letting go her hand.

'Surely I heard a sort of little screaming squeak under those sacks? Why, you've been carrying corn, and there's mice in this waggon, I declare!' She began to haul up the tails of her gown.

'Oh no; 'tis the axle,' said Tony in an assuring way. 'It do go like that sometimes in dry weather.'

'Perhaps it was ... Well, now, to be quite honest, dear Tony, do you like her better than me? Because—because, although I've held off so independent, I'll own at last that I do like 'ee, Tony, to tell the truth; and I wouldn't say no if you asked me—you know that.'

Tony was so won over by this pretty offering mood of a girl who had been quite the reverse (Hannah had a backward way with her at times, if you can mind) that he just glanced behind, and then whispered very soft, I haven't quite promised her, and I think I can get out of it, and ask you that question you speak of.'

'Throw over Milly?—all to marry me! How delightful!' broke out Hannah, quite loud, clapping her hands.

At this there was a real squeak—an angry, spiteful squeak, and afterward a long moan, as if something had broke its heart, and a movement of the empty sacks.

'Something's there!' said Hannah, starting up.

'It's nothing, really,' says Tony in a soothing voice, and praying inwardly for a way out of this. 'I wouldn't tell 'ee at first, because I wouldn't frighten 'ee. But, Hannah, I've really a couple of ferrets in a bag under there, for rabbiting, and they quarrel sometimes. I don't wish it knowed, as 'twould be called poaching. Oh, they can't get out, bless 'ee—you are quite safe! And—and—what a fine day it is, isn't it, Hannah, for this time of year? Be you going to market next Saturday? How is your aunt now?' And so on, says Tony, to keep her from talking any more about love in Milly's hearing.

But he found his work cut out for him, and wondering again how he should get out of this ticklish business, he looked about for a chance. Nearing home he saw his father in a field not far off, holding up his hand as if he wished to speak to Tony.

'Would you mind taking the reins a moment, Hannah,' he said, much relieved, 'while I go and find out what father wants?'

She consented, and away he hastened into the field, only

too glad to get breathing time. He found that his father was looking at him with rather a stern eye.

'Come, come Tony,' says old Mr Kytes, as soon as his son was alongside him, 'this won't do, you know.'

'What?' says Tony.

'Why, if you mean to marry Milly Richards, do it, and there's an end o't. But don't go driving about the country with Jolliver's daughter and making a scandal. I won't have such things done.'

'I only asked her—that is, she asked me, to ride home.'

'She? Why, now, if it had been Milly, 'twould have been quite proper; but you and Hannah Jolliver going about by yourselves—'

'Milly's there too, father.'

'Milly? Where?'

'Under the corn-sacks! Yes, the truth is, father, I've got rather into a nunnywatch, I'm afeared! Unity Sallet is there too—yes, at the other end, under the tarpaulin. All three are in that waggon, and what to do with 'em I know no more than the dead! The best plan is, as I'm thinking, to speak out loud and plain to one of 'em before the rest, and that will settle it; not but what 'twill cause 'em to kick up a bit of a miff, for certain. Now which would you marry, father, if you was in my place?'

'Whichever of 'em did *not* ask to ride with thee.'

'That was Milly, I'm bound to say, as she only mounted by my invitation. But Milly—'

'Then stick to Milly, she's the best. . . . But look at that!'

His father pointed toward the waggon. 'She can't hold that horse in. You shouldn't have left the reins in her hands. Run on and take the horse's head, or there'll be some accident to them maids!'

Tony's horse, in fact, in spite of Hannah's tugging at the reins, had started on his way at a brisk walking pace, being very anxious to get back to the stable, for he had had a long day out. Without another word Tony rushed away from his father to overtake the horse.

Now of all things that could have happened to wean him from Milly there was nothing so powerful as his father recommending her. No; it could not be Milly, after all.

Hannah must be the one, since he could not marry all three as he longed to do. This he thought while running after the waggon. But queer things were happening inside it.

It was, of course, Milly who had screamed under the sack-bags, being obliged to let off her bitter rage and shame in that way at what Tony was saying, and never daring to show, for very pride and dread o' being laughed at, that she was in hiding. She became more and more restless, and in twisting herself about, what did she see but another woman's foot and white stocking close to her head. It quite frightened her, not knowing that Unity Sallet was in the waggon likewise. But after the fright was over she determined to get to the bottom of all this, and she crept and crept along the bed of the waggon, under the tarpaulin, like a snake, when lo and behold she came face to face with Unity.

'Well, if this isn't disgraceful!' says Milly in a raging whisper to Unity.

' 'Tis,' says Unity, 'to see you hiding in a young man's waggon like this, and no great character belonging to either of ye!'

'Mind what you are saying!' replied Milly, getting louder. 'I am engaged to be married to him, and haven't I a right to be here? What right have you, I should like to know? What has he been promising you? A pretty lot of nonsense, I expect! But what Tony says to other women is all mere wind, and no concern to me!'

'Don't you be too sure!' says Unity. 'He's going to have Hannah, and not you, nor me either; I could hear that.'

Now at these strange voices sounding from under the cloth Hannah was thunderstruck almost into a swound; and it was just at the time that the horse moved on. Hannah tugged away wildly, not knowing what she was doing; and as the quarrel rose louder and louder Hannah got so horrified that she let go the reins altogether. The horse went on at his own pace, and coming to the corner where we turn round to drop down the hill to Lower Longpuddle he turned too quick, the off wheels went on the bank, the waggon rose sideways till it was quite on edge upon the near axles, and out rolled the three maidens into the road in a heap. The horse looked round and stood still.

When Tony came up, frightened and breathless, he was relieved enough to see that none of his darlings was hurt, beyond a few scratches from the brambles of the hedge. But he was rather alarmed when he heard how they were going on at one another.

'Don't ye quarrel, my dears—don't ye!' says he, taking off his hat out of respect to 'em. And then he would have kissed them all round, as fair and square as a man could, but they were in too much of a taking to let him, and screeched and sobbed till they were quite spent.

'Now I'll speak out honest, because I ought to,' says Tony as soon as he could get heard. 'And this is the truth,' says he. 'I've asked Hannah to be mine, and she is willing, and we are going to put up the banns next—'

Tony had not noticed that Hannah's father was coming up behind, nor had he noticed that Hannah's face was beginning to bleed from the scratch of a bramble. Hannah had seen her father, and had run to him, crying worse than ever.

'My daughter is *not* willing, sir!' said Mr Jolliver hot and strong. 'Be you willing, Hannah? I ask ye to have spirit enough to refuse him!'

'I have spirit, and I do refuse him!' says Hannah, partly because her father was there, and partly, too, in a tantrum because of the discovery, and the scar that might be left on her face. 'Little did I think when I was so soft with him just now that I was talking to such a false deceiver!'

'What, you won't have me, Hannah?' says Tony, his jaw hanging down like a dead man's.

'Never—I would sooner marry no-nobody at all!' she gasped out, though with her heart in her throat, for she would not have refused Tony if he had asked her quietly, and her father had not been there, and her face had not been scratched by the bramble. And having said that, away she walked upon her father's arm, thinking and hoping he would ask her again.

Tony didn't know what to say next. Milly was sobbing her heart out; but as his father had strongly recommended her he couldn't feel inclined that way. So he turned to Unity.

'Well, will you, Unity dear, be mine?' he says.

'Take her leavings? Not I!' says Unity. 'I'd scorn it!' And away walks Unity Sallet likewise, though she looked back when she'd gone some way, to see if he was following her.

So there at last were left Milly and Tony by themselves, she crying in watery streams, and Tony looking like a tree struck by lightning.

'Well, Milly,' he says at last, going up to her, 'it do seem as if fate had ordained that it should be you and I, or nobody. And what must be must be, I suppose. Hey, Milly?'

'If you like, Tony. You didn't really mean what you said to them?'

'Not a word of it!' declares Tony, bringing down his fist upon his palm.

And then he kissed her, and put the waggon to rights, and they mounted together; and their banns were put up the very next Sunday. I was not able to go to their wedding, but it was a rare party they had, by all account.

And Man *by William Saroyan*

One morning, when I was fifteen, I got up before daybreak, because all night I hadn't been able to sleep, tossing in bed with the thought of the earth and the strangeness of being alive, suddenly feeling myself a part of it, definitely, solidly. Merely to be standing again, I had thought all night. Merely to be in the light again, standing, breathing, being alive. I left my bed quietly in the darkness of early morning and put on my clothes, a blue cotton shirt, a pair of corduroy pants, stockings and shoes. It was November and it was beginning to turn cold, but I did not wish to put on more clothes. I felt warm enough. I felt almost feverish, and with more clothes I knew it would not happen. Something was going to happen, and I felt that if I put on too many clothes it would dwindle away and all that I would have would be the remembrance of something expected, then lost.

All through the sleeplessness of the night I could feel turning in me, like a multitude of small and large wheels, some swift and wordless thought, on the verge of articulation, some vast remembrance out of time, a fresh fullness, a new solidity, a more graceful rhythm of motion emerging from the hurried growth that had taken place in me during the summer.

With the beginning of spring that year came the faint and fragmentary beginning of this thought, burning in my mind with the sound of fire eating substance, sweeping through my blood with the impatience and impetuosity of a deluge. Before the beginning of this thought I had been nothing more than a small and sullen boy, moving through the moments of my life with anger and fear and bitterness and doubt, wanting desperately to know the meaning and never quite being able to do so. But now in November I was as large physically as a man, larger, for that matter, than most men. It was as if I had leaped suddenly from the form of myself as a boy to the vaster form of myself as a man, and to the vaster meaning of myself as something specific and alive. Look at him, my relatives were saying, every part of his body is growing, especially his nose.

And they made sly jokes about my private organs, driving me out of my head with shame. How about it? they asked, even the ladies. Is it growing? Do you dream of big women, hundreds of them?

I don't know what you're talking about, I used to say. But I did know. Only I was ashamed. Look at that nose, they used to say. Just look at that enormous nose on his face.

During the summer I sometimes stopped suddenly before a mirror to look at myself, and after a moment I would turn away feeling disgusted with my ugliness, worrying about it. I couldn't understand how it was that I looked utterly unlike what I imagined myself to be. In my mind I had another face, a finer, a more subtle and dignified expression, but in the mirror I could see the real reflection of myself, and I could see that it was ugly, thick, bony and coarse. I thought it was something finer, I used to say to myself. I hadn't bothered before about looking at myself. I had thought that I knew precisely how I looked, and the truth distressed me, making me ashamed. Afterwards I stopped caring. I am ugly, I said. I know I am ugly. But it is only my face.

And I could believe that my face was not the whole of it. It was simply a part of myself that was growing with the rest, an outward part, and therefore not as important as the inward part. The real growth was going on inside, not simply within the boundaries of my physical form, but outward through the mind and through the imagination to the real largeness of being, the limitless largeness of consciousness, of knowing and feeling and remembering.

I began to forget the ugliness of my face, turning again to the simplicity and kindliness of the face I believed to be my own, the face of myself in the secrecy of my heart, in the night light of sleep, in the truth of thought.

It is true that my face seems ugly, I said, but it is also true that it is not ugly. I know it is not, because I have seen it with my own eyes and shaped it with my own thought, and my vision has been clear and my thought has been clean. It cannot be ugly.

But how was anyone to understand the real truth, how was anyone to see the face I saw, and know that it was the real reflection of my being? This worried me a lot. There was a girl in my class at high school whom I worshipped, and I wanted this girl to see that my face, the face she saw, was not the truthful one, that it was merely a part of the growth that was going on. And I wanted her to be able to see with me the truthful face, because I felt that if she did see it, she would understand my love for her, and she would love me.

All through the night I had tossed with the thought of myself somehow alive on the earth, somehow specific and at the same time a substance that was changing and would always change, from moment to moment, imperceptibly, myself entering one moment thus, and emerging thus, over and over again. I wanted to know what it was in me that was static and permanent and endurable, what it was that belonged not to myself alone but to the body of man, to his legend, to the truth of his motion over the earth, moment after moment, century after century. All through the night it seemed that I would soon learn, and in the morning I left my bed, standing in the darkness and the stillness, feeling the splendour of having form and weight and motion, having, I hoped, meaning.

I walked quietly through the darkness of the house and emerged, standing for a moment in the street, acknowledging the magnificence of our earth, the large beauty of limitless space about our insignificant forms, the remoteness of the great celestial bodies of our universe, our oceans, our mountains, our valleys, the great cities we had made, the strong and clean and fearless things we had done. The small boats we had made and sent over the wild waters, the slow growth of railroads, the slow accumulation of knowledge, the slow but everlasting seeking after God, in the vastness of the universe, in the solidity of our own earth, in the glory of our own small beings, the simplicity of our own hearts.

Merely to be standing, merely to be breathing that day was a truth in the nature of an inexplicable miracle. After all these years, I thought. . . I myself standing here in the darkness, breathing, knowing that I live. I wanted to say something in language, with the words I had been taught in school, some-thing solemn and dignified and joyous . . . to express the gratitude I felt to God. But it was impossible. There were no words with which to say it. I could feel the magnificence coming through the cold clean air, touching my blood, racing through it, dancing, but there were no words with which to say it.

There was a fire hydrant in our street, and I had always wanted to hurdle it, but I had always been afraid to try. The hydrant was made of metal and my substance was of flesh and bone and blood, and if I did not clear the hydrant, leaping swiftly, my flesh would smash against it, paining me, perhaps breaking a bone in one of my legs.

Suddenly I was leaping over the hydrant, and, clearing it, I was thinking, I can do it now. I can do anything now.

I hurdled the fire hydrant six or seven times, leaping away over it, hearing myself landing solidly on the earth, feeling tremendous.

Then I began to walk, not slowly, not casually, but vigorously, leaping now and then because I couldn't help it. Each time I came to a tree, I leaped and caught a limb, making it bend with my weight, pulling myself up and letting myself down. I walked into the town, into the streets where we had put up our buildings, and suddenly I saw them for this first time, suddenly I was really *seeing* them, and they were splendid. The city was almost deserted, and I alone in it, its only inhabitant, seeing it as it really was, in all its fineness, with all its meaning, giving it its real truth, like the truth of my hidden face, the inward splendour. The winter sun came up while I walked and its light fell over the city, making a cool warmth. I touched the buildings, feeling them with the palms of my hands, feeling the meaning of the solidity and the precision. I touched the plate-glass windows, the brick, the wood and the cement.

When I got home, everyone was awake, at the breakfast table. Where have you been? they asked. Why did you get up so early?

I sat in my chair at the table, feeling great hunger. Shall I tell them? I thought. Shall I try to tell them what is happening? Will they understand? Or will they laugh at me?

Suddenly I knew I was a stranger among them, my own people, and I knew that while I loved them, I could not go out to them, revealing the truth of my being. Each of us is alone, I thought. Each is a stranger to the other. My mother thinks of me as a pain she once suffered, a babe at her breast, a small child in the house, a boy walking to school, and now a young man with an ugly face, a restless and half-mad fellow who moves about strangely.

We ate mush in those days. It was cheap and we were poor, and the mush filled a lot of space. We used to buy it in bulk, by the pound, and we had it for breakfast every morning. There was a big bowl of it before me, about a pound and a half of it, steaming, and I began to swallow the food, feeling it sinking to my hunger, entering my blood, becoming myself and the change that was going on in me.

No, I thought. I cannot tell them. I cannot tell anyone. Everyone must see for himself. Everyone must seek the truth for himself. It is here, and each man must seek it for himself. But the girl, I thought. I should be able to tell her. She was of me. I had taken her name, her form, the outward one and the inward one, and I had breathed her being into my being, joining her meaning to my meaning, and she was of my thought, of my motion in walking over the earth, and of my sleep. I would tell her. After I had revealed my hidden face to her, I would speak to the girl about ourselves, about our being alive together, on the same earth, in the same moment of eternity. I had never spoken to the girl. I had loved her secretly, worshipping her, worshipping the very things she touched, her books, her desk, the earth over which she moved, the air about her, but I had never had the courage to speak to her. I wanted my speaking to mean so much, to be so important to each of us, that I was afraid even to think of breaking the silence between us.

I went for a little walk, I replied.

Everyone began to laugh at me, even my mother. What's the matter with you? they asked. Why can't you sleep? Are you in love again? Is that it? Are you dreaming of some girl?

I sat at the table, swallowing the hot food, hearing their laughter. I cannot tell them, I thought. They are laughing at me. They think it is something to laugh about. They think it is a little joke.

I began to blush, thinking of the girl and worrying about something to say that would satisfy and silence them, stopping their laughter. Then they began to laugh louder than ever, and I couldn't help it, I began to laugh too.

Yes, they laughed. It must be some girl. Look how handsome he is getting to be. Dreaming about a girl always does that.

I ate all the mush in the bowl and got up from the table. If I try to tell them the truth, I thought, they will laugh more than ever.

I'm going to school, I said, and I left the house. But I knew I would not go to school that day. I had decided not to go in the middle of the night, when I had been unable to sleep. In school, in that atmosphere, it would never happen. I would never be able to understand what it was that turned in me, circling toward truth, and it would be lost, maybe for ever. I decided to walk into the country and be alone with the thought, helping it to emerge from the bewilderment and confusion of my mind and the fever of my blood, carrying it to silence and simplicity, giving it a chance to reach its fullness and be whole.

Walking through the country, moving quietly among the leafless grape vines and fig trees, the thought became whole, and I knew the truth about myself and man and the earth and God.

At the proper hour I returned home, as if I were coming home from school, and the following day I went to school. I knew I would be asked for an excuse and an explanation for my absence, and I knew I would not lie about it. I could tell them I had been at home, sick with a cold, but I didn't want to do it. There would be a punishment, but I didn't care about that. Let them punish me if they liked. Let old man Brunton give me a strapping. I had walked into the country, into the silence, and I had found the truth. It was more than anything they would ever be able to teach. It was something that wasn't in any of their books. Let them punish me. I wanted also to impress the girl. I wanted her to understand that I had strength, that I could tell the truth and be punished for it, that I would not make up a cheap lie just to get out of a strapping. My telling the truth ought to mean something to her, I thought. Being so much a part of myself, she would be able to see beneath the surface and understand what I had done, and why.

After the roll was taken, my name was called and our

teacher said: You were not at school yesterday. Have you brought an excuse?

No, I said, I have not.

Suddenly I felt myself to be the object of the laughter of everyone in the classroom, and I could imagine everyone thinking: What a stupid fellow! I looked at this girl whom I loved so much and I saw that she too was laughing, but I would not believe it. This sometimes happens. It happens when a man has given another person his own dignity and meaning, and the other person has not acquired that dignity and meaning. I saw and heard the girl laughing at me, but I would not believe it. I hadn't intended to entertain her. I hadn't intended to entertain anyone, and the laughter made me angry.

Why were you away from school? said the teacher. Where were you?

I was in the country, I said, walking.

Now the laughter was greater than ever, and I saw the girl I secretly loved laughing with the others, as if I meant nothing to her, as if I hadn't made her a part of myself. I began to feel ill and defiant, and there was warm perspiration on the palms of my hands.

The teacher stood over me, trembling. One must, perhaps, be a teacher to be able to appreciate precisely how angry she felt. For years she had been asking boys why they had been absent from school, and for years the boys had replied that they had been at home, ill. She had known that in most cases they had not told the truth, but the tradition had been maintained and everything had remained solid in her world. Now everything was being shattered, and she was standing over me, trembling with rage. I think she tried to shake me, and I would not let her do it, holding myself solidly. For a moment she budged at me, hating me, and then she said, You Armenians, you, you . . . and I thought she would burst into tears. I felt sorry for her, for the stupidity she had preserved in herself after so many years of trying to teach school, a woman almost fifty years of age.

And I hadn't meant to hurt her. That hadn't been my object at all. I had meant simply to tell the truth. I had meant to reveal to the girl my true face, the face which had been shaped

by the dignity and simplicity of man and which she had helped
to shape, and I had meant to reveal to her the truth of my
presence on earth. And then her laughter, just like the laughter
of the others . . . it mangled something in me, and I stood in
the midst of the noise, embarrassed and bewildered, bleeding,
and breaking to pieces. Damn it, I thought. This is not true.
Damn it, this is a lie.

But I knew I was deceiving myself. And I knew I would
never be able to speak to the girl about my love for her, and
the meaning of that love to me, and to the earth and the
universe, and to man.

I was sent to the principal of the school, and he stood over
me, grumbling in a deep voice. You, he said, you are a disgrace
to this school. You are a disgrace to your own race. You break
rules. Then you come to school flaunting your crime. What
have you to say for yourself?

Nothing, I said.

Why did you do it? he asked.

I wanted to walk, I said.

You could have waited till Saturday, he said.

No, I said. I had to walk yesterday.

Can you think of any reason why I shouldn't strap you? he
asked.

That's up to you, I said.

I was angry. I felt bitter about the girl, and I wasn't afraid
of the principal or of the strapping I knew he would give me.
It was all over. I would have to walk alone with the secret.
I would have to accept the sickness in me that the girl had
made by laughing, but the truth would remain whole and I
would have it to keep for ever, walking alone, in the secrecy of
my heart.

The strapping made me cry, big as I was, strong as I was.
While I cried, though, I knew it wasn't the strapping that
was hurting me . . . it was this other thing, this incredible
blindness everywhere. I cried bitterly, and when I returned to
class my eyes were red and I was ashamed, and the whole class
was laughing at me, even the girl.

After school, walking alone, I tried to heal the wound in my
heart, and I began to think again of the swift and bright truth
of being, the truth I had earned for myself by walking alone

through the silence of the earth, and walking, thinking of it, I could feel myself becoming whole again, and I could hear myself laughing through the vastness of the secret space I had discovered.

The truth was the secret, God first, the word, the word God, out of all things and beyond, spaceless and timeless, then the void, the silent emptiness, vaster than any mortal mind could conceive, abstract and precise and real and lost, the substance in the emptiness, again precise and with weight and solidity and form, fire and fluid, and then, walking through the vineyards, I had seen it thus, the whole universe, quietly there in the mind of man, motionless and dark and lost, waiting for man, for the thought of man, and I felt the stirring of inanimate substance in the earth and in myself like the swift growth of the summer, life emerging from time, the germ of man springing from the rock and the fire and the fluid to the face of man, and to the form, to the motion and the thought, suddenly in the emptiness, the thought of man, stirring there. And *I* was man, and this was the truth I had brought out of the emptiness, walking alone through the vineyards.

I had seen the universe, quietly in the emptiness, secret, and I had revealed it to itself, giving it meaning and grace and the truth that could come only from the thought and energy of man, and the truth was man, myself, moment after moment, and man, century after century, and man, and the face of God in man, and the sound of the laughter of man in the vastness of the secret, and the sound of his weeping in the darkness of it, and the truth was myself and I was man.

Death of the Zulu by Uys *Krige*

It was about two hours after our capture. We were marching from Figtree towards Tobruk port. It was midsummer, the sun well up, but, thank God, not too hot yet—though I knew by the brittle cobalt look of the sky that it would not be long before the heat would become unbearable, beating down upon that bone-dry earth in shimmering, scorching waves. . . . We weren't doing anything, not even thinking, just trudging along, dragging our heavy feet through the sand, raising the dust in yellowish-grey clouds in the dips and in little lingering puffs round our boots on the straight.

I appeared to have two minds: the one stunned, the other perfectly conscious, taking in coolly and dispassionately our surroundings. Only one sight was clear-cut, vivid: that silent mob of men streaming towards Tobruk. And only one sound audible: the click or scrunch of desert boots when we struck a rock vein or a loose surface of grit across our path.

Those boots, that everlasting dragging, clogged tramp, tramp, tramp. . . . Like a drum. . . . Like the slow, dull, monotonous beat of a drum. And with a single monotonous refrain: out of nothing, through nothing, towards nothing . . . Out of nothing: the thunderous vacuum of the battle. Through nothing: this strange, unreal scene, as if flickering in a film. Towards nothing: the huge inconceivable emptiness of our life of captivity and exile to come. . . .

It would be more accurate to say I seemed to have, not two minds, but three, the third listening to a monologue by the conscious mind. 'Yes, before it often seemed to you,' it was saying, 'that you were living only in the past or the future, never in the present. The present was always escaping you, slipping like sand through your fingers. Now you have your present, my boy, and a fine present it is too! Very present, very real . . . And you can't barricade yourself against it by drawing on your memories. They've been washed out. Nor can you throw up a rampart against it with hopes, plans for the future. For your future, too, has gone down the drain. There is

no past. There is no future. There's only the present. . . .'
There were bodies lying beside the road, some singly, some in batches. Dead or wounded, I didn't look, I wasn't interested. My eyes slid over them as if they were so many pieces of old motor junk scattered about a disused yard somewhere. 'They're dead and they've a wife like you. . . .' I heard a faint voice whisper somewhere far off. 'They're dead and they've a mother like you. . . .' The voice was taking shape, getting stronger. 'They're dead and they've a child like you. . . .' The voice now was quite loud. It was my unconscious mind awaking; and the monologue had become a dialogue.

'I don't care a damn. . . .' I heard the calm mind say, but it was fast losing its imperturbability. 'Let them all go to hell. . . . Let them all go straight to hell! I don't care a damn!'

Below the escarpment the track we were following made a curve. I was on the left-hand side of the curve when I heard a shout. Mechanically I looked up. To the right, in the curve's bulge, about fifty yards away, a German officer was standing over someone stretched out on the ground. He shouted again, beckoned with his arm. Though there must have been at least a dozen men in our group, numbly, apathetically, I thought: 'It's me he wants, he's looking straight at me, I can see the blue of his eyes. . . .'

Automatically I stepped off the track. There were two other South Africans beside me also walking towards the German. I did not know who they were, I had never seen them before. They must have been beside me—or just behind me—during that long, weary trek from Figtree, but I hadn't noticed them. It was only now, as one on each side of me, they too moved forward towards the officer and the figure at his feet, that their presence began impinging upon my consciousness. And though I was to spend at least a quarter of an hour in their company I cannot, to this day, recollect a single feature or physical characteristic of either of them.

The next minute I was standing beside the man lying on the ground. It was one of our native soldiers and I could tell by his build and features that he was a Zulu. As a Government official in Natal for some years, I had got to know this noble race, their language and customs well. A shell must have burst near him. His left arm was off at the elbow. A large splinter

53

must have snapped it off as one snaps crisply and cleanly between one's fingers a dried mealie stalk. His shirt, I noticed, was full of little craters, stiff with caked blood.

Then I saw his eyes. They were a luminous jet black, stricken with pain; yet they seemed, somehow, detached. Although the man was looking straight at me he appeared unaware of my presence.

'*Kuyini umfana?* (What is it, young Zulu?)' I asked, bending over him and hearing my voice go trailing over the sand with a gruff undertone as if this were yet another imbecility for which I wasn't in the least responsible and I resented being implicated in it; as if what that droning voice really wanted to say was: 'I'm out of it, do you hear? Out of it. . . . Leave me alone! Why drag me back? Why—'

Hearing his own language, the young Zulu raised his head slightly. His eyes seemed brighter, but their expression had changed; it was no longer remote, had become intimate. Then his head fell back, his eyes however, never leaving my face. '*Hawu . . . umlungu . . .*' he groaned. '*Kubi . . . Insimbi ingishayili. . . .* (O . . . white man . . . It is not a good thing. . . . The iron has hit me. . . .)'

Suddenly I realized I was normal again, with my mind no longer split into segments, but an integrated whole with perfectly logical perceptions and reactions.

I had come erect, was looking around. The German officer had gone. About four hundred yards away I saw him, driving away in his truck. I turned to the Zulu again. He was in a half sitting position with one of the two men who had stepped out of our lines with me, crouched down behind him, holding him up.

'How do you feel, *umfana*?' I asked going down on my right knee. A hard glitter came into his eyes, then he said slowly, clearly: '*Umlungu, ngidubule. . . .* (White man, shoot me. . . .)' There was no doubting it, he was pleading with me— apparently unaware that I, like him, was now a prisoner no longer carrying a weapon and therefore as powerless as he against his fate.

'Don't talk like that, *umfana*,' I said peremptorily, more to get a grip on myself than to rebuke him. 'You've only lost an arm. Many men have lost an arm, and they're walking about now, laughing, with their heads in the sun.'

'*Cha . . . Cha . . .* (No . . . no . . .)' he muttered, almost angrily.

'Yes, yes . . .' I continued, speaking fast. 'We'll get a doctor for you and we'll take you to the hospital'—We, we, who the hell's we, I thought, we're nothing, less than nothing—'and they'll be good to you there, soon you'll be a whole man again and it won't be many moons before you'll be going about your work, watching the pumpkins fill out, the maize swell in the cob, and the cattle grow fat in the fields back in Zululand. . . .'

I do not know what made me say this. I knew it wasn't true. My own words, with a hollow false sound, echoed back on my ears.

'*Cha, umlungu . . . Ngidubule! Ngidubule!* (No, white man . . . shoot me! Shoot me!)' How strong his voice is, I thought, out of all proportion to his strength.

'Soon,' I repeated, 'You'll be a whole man again.'

'No, no, white man. . . .' He was shaking his head in exactly the way I had so often seen old Zulu indunas shake their heads, when in tribal councils they would, by their whole expression and attitude, gently but firmly convey to the European that the sum of all his knowledge was as nothing compared with their ancient African wisdom. '*Ngiphelile* . . . (I am finished . . .).'

A little desert car drew up twenty yards away. A tall, thin German officer with sharp features jumped out and was beside us in a few quick darting steps. Another German officer, short and squat, had followed him—and the next moment, the tall officer was bending over the African, feeling his chest beneath the blood-stiffened shirt. Noticing his stars and the snake of Aesculapius in his badge, I felt at once, greatly relieved.

I looked at the Zulu's arm again. Most of the stump's end was caked over with dry, hardened blood. It still bled, but very little, only a trickle oozing through the shattered flesh.

'*Ngidubule!*' His voice was no longer supplicating but had a fierce, ringing quality as if raised in protest that this was no extravagant demand but a fitting and just claim upon me. My gaze travelled over his magnificent body. The broad torso bulged beneath the army shirt. The thighs, curving into sight under the dirty bloodstained shorts, were of a classic symmetry, the calves and legs as harmoniously proportionate.

Then the thought struck me that the Zulus, physically, are

one of the most beautiful races in the world; that Zulu males have an extraordinary pride in their physique; that they consider any deformity of the body—and particularly disfigurement—as something unnatural, even monstrous; and that formerly they killed all children unfortunate enough to be born cripples. Naturally this young Zulu, descended from generations of warriors, wanted to die now, clamoured for death; for this cracked useless body, this stump of an arm, were they not a shame and a disgrace, a crying offence against both man and the gods?

My eyes slipped over his chest again, met his. I knew they had never left my face even though the German doctor was still bending over him examining him, feeling tentatively for his wounds. Now, quite simply, as if he had read my thoughts and was confident that his wish would be granted, he said slowly: '*Ngidubule, umlungu. . . .*'

'No, you speak foolish things.'

'*Ngidubule!*' The short spell of calm had broken, the voice was again urgent. Did it contain a note of reproach?

'*Ngidubule, umlungu, ngidubule!*' Yes, it was reproachful. God would that eternal cry of '*Ngidubule . . .*' never stop?

The doctor had pulled out his hand, turned and was looking at me.

'What does he say?' he asked me in German.

'It is his request that we shoot him . . .' I answered, realising at once that I was giving a stiff literal German translation not of what the Zulu had said but of what his headman would have said in slow solemn tone to the other assembled members of the tribe were they here now, squatting in a half circle round the dying man, deliberating his case.

Whether the Zulu finally understood that I could not, would not do it, or whether he recognised the German doctor as his enemy who, according to his subconscious reasoning, would be less averse to such an action, I do not know; but as soon as he had heard this new, foreign voice intruding upon our dialogue, he was no longer looking at me but at the German.

Leaning up against the South African supporting him from behind, he had had until now his right hand on the ground. But now, in a great effort, his lips twitching in pain—there were foam flecks on them, spotted with blood—he brought his right hand to his shirt front and slowly, gropingly, uncovered his chest. Next, straining himself forward, he said in a deep resonant voice to the German captain: '*Wena awungidubule!*' (You shoot me). Strange, but at that moment it sounded almost like a command.

'He wants you to shoot him. . . .' I told the doctor. Standing stiffly beside me, the German made no reply.

'What chance has he of living?' I asked.

'None,' came the incisive answer. 'He must have been wounded yesterday afternoon, has lain here all night. He's lost so much blood, he can't have much more to lose. Had he been a European he would have been dead long ago. . . .' His voice was as jerky as his movements.

Though speaking German, we had instinctively moved a few paces away as if afraid the wounded man would understand.

'And he still speaks,' the voice staccatoed on, 'with all that shrapnel inside him! He'll probably die when we move him. Then again, he's so strong he might live for hours.'

I turned to the African. 'The doctor says you are badly hurt, but that you have great strength, and must not worry. We're going to carry you to that truck, take you to the hospital.'

'No, no . . . I am finished . . . Shoot me . . . I cannot live any more. The pain is too deep . . . *umlungu*. . . .' He was groaning again, his voice getting weaker, and for the first time he closed his eyes for longer than a second. His hand, too, had fallen back on the ground, black against the pale yellow earth.

The doctor touched me on the arm. 'Perhaps it would be the easiest way out,' he said, and motioned to the young lieutenant standing a few paces away. An order from the captain, and the lieutenant had pulled out his pistol and handed it to me. I stood there, as if petrified, with the pistol in my right hand.

'*Umlungu . . . umlungu . . .*' were the only two words now uttered by the Zulu lying at my feet with closed eyes and quivering lips. He kept on muttering them, his voice never rising above a whisper. Yet the repeated '*umlungu . . . umlungu . . .*' seemed to contain a note of awe, almost of reverence—not, I felt, because I was an officer and he a private, but because at that moment I must have appeared to his bewildered mind, half crazed with pain, the great benefactor bearing in my hands the supreme gift of peace and the healing oblivion of death.

I looked from the pistol to the captain, from the captain back to the pistol, then at the Zulu. He in the meanwhile, had opened his eyes.

'*Ngidubule!*' his voice rang in my ears, as strong as ever. I shook my head. 'No,' I said to the captain, handing him the pistol, 'I do not shoot my friends.'

It was at least two seconds before I realised I had addressed the German in Zulu.

The Zulu's gaze had followed the motion of the pistol; he now stared at the captain. The German stood, irresolute, as if embarrassed by the pistol. He seemed to be debating a point. Then turning to me, he said:

'My business is to preserve life not to destroy it.'

'And not to lessen pain?'

'Yes, to lessen pain.' He was speaking much more slowly; the bark had gone out of his voice. 'But that would be contrary to Red Cross regulations. I'm not even allowed to carry firearms. . . .' This typical German respect for rules and regulations, I thought, how incongruous!

The next moment the captain had handed the pistol back to its owner. 'Herr Oberleutnant Muller,' he rapped out in military tone: 'Shoot this man!'

Then I noticed the Zulu's hand come creeping up his chest again and I forgot everything, watching it, fascinated. It was a broad compact hand with a fair-sized wart on the index finger and at that moment it seemed to pulse with life, to be one of the most living things I had ever seen. The big strong fingers felt for the edge of the shirt-front where the V-opening ended, closed over it in a firm grip; there was a quick sharp rip of khaki drill tearing, and the shirt fell apart, revealing the entire chest. The right side had hardly been touched but the left, until now concealed by the shirt, was a mass of torn flesh.

I looked away. The lieutenant had stepped forward, was standing a few feet from the Zulu. He had a set look on his face, holding the weapon stiffly in front of him, pointing it at the dying man.

The Zulu's hand was buried deep in the sand, gripping the earth, supporting his body. To me, at that moment, it seemed that in a last superhuman effort he wanted to lift himself, rise and with both feet planted firmly on the ground, meet his death face to face. He had squared his shoulders, throwing them back and was straining his chest out and up, as if to present a better target to the enemy, or to thrust it against the very muzzle of the pistol.

Now his eyes were ablaze as if all the fierce passionate life that remained to him were concentrated in their jet-black depths.

'*Ngidubule! Ngidubule!*' broke from his dry, cracked lips in a crescendo, like a shout of joy, a triumphant roar; and I was reminded of the Zulu battle cry I had so often heard, sonorous and barbaric, bursting from a thousand throats when the war dance reaches its frenzied, crashing climax.

'*Ngidubule! Ngidubule!*'

Yes, he was roaring at his body, roaring at his pain, roaring at death.

Rooted to the spot, I stood looking down at him. I wanted to tear myself away. I couldn't.

Carefully, methodically, the lieutenant took aim along the pistol barrel.

I felt a hand clutch my shoulder. For a second it lay there, lax. Then it tightened over my collarbone. I half turned. It was the captain. Slowly he turned me completely round. He took a step forward. I followed. I was waiting, I felt, for yet another '*Ngidubule!*' rather than the pistol's report; and when a snail-shell (one of those countless bone-white shells scattered like tiny skulls about the desert) popped under my feet, I shuddered.

We were about fifteen feet away when the pistol cracked. It did not go off again.

I have a very hazy recollection of what happened after that.

I remember the German captain saying, '*Auf wiedersehen*'; the two officers driving off in the small car; and that for a long time I sat on a flat stone beside the road.

Legs, many legs, milled past, kept slipping in and out of my vision. But they made no impression on me; in a dull, disconnected way I was more interested in the little wisps of sand that kept spiralling, circling about my boots and then settling in a thin, pale yellow dust on the broad square toecaps.

How long I sat there, staring at my boots, I don't know. Someone shouted in Afrikaans: 'Come along, Du Toit! Come along!' and when I found myself again, I was once more among that crowd of prisoners tramping slowly, wearily towards Tobruk.

The Rocking-Horse Winner

by D H Lawrence

There was a woman who was beautiful, who started with all the advantages, yet she had no luck. She married for love, and the love turned to dust. She had bonny children, yet she felt they had been thrust upon her, and she could not love them. They looked at her coldly, as if they were finding fault with her. And hurriedly she felt she must cover up some fault in herself. Yet what it was that she must cover up she never knew. Nevertheless, when her children were present, she always felt the centre of her heart go hard. This troubled her, and in her manner she was all the more gentle and anxious for her children, as if she loved them very much. Only she herself knew that at the centre of her heart was a hard little place that could not feel love, no, not for anybody. Everybody else said of her: 'She is such a good mother. She adores her children.' Only she herself, and her children themselves, knew it was not so. They read it in each other's eyes.

There was a boy and two little girls. They lived in a pleasant house, with a garden, and they had discreet servants, and felt themselves superior to anyone in the neighbourhood.

Although they lived in style, they felt always an anxiety in the house. There was never enough money. The mother had a small income, and the father had a small income, but not nearly enough for the social position which they had to keep up. The father went into town to some office. But though he had good prospects, these prospects never materialised. There was always the grinding sense of the shortage of money, though the style was always kept up.

At last, the mother said: 'I will see if I can't make something.' But she did not know where to begin. She racked her brains, and tried this thing and the other, but could not find anything successful. The failure made deep lines come into her face. Her children were growing up, they would have to go to school. There must be more money, there must be more money. The father, who was always very handsome and expensive in his tastes, seemed as if he never would be able to do anything worth doing. And the mother, who had a great belief in herself, did not succeed any better, and her tastes were just as expensive.

And so the house came to be haunted by the unspoken phrase: *There must be more money! There must be more money!* The children could hear it all the time, though nobody said it aloud. They heard it at Christmas, when the expensive and splendid toys filled the nursery. Behind the shining modern rocking-horse, behind the smart doll's house, a voice would start whispering: 'There *must* be more money! There *must* be more money!' And the children would stop playing, to listen for a moment. They would look into each other's eyes, to see if they had all heard. And each one saw in the eyes of the other two that they had heard. 'There *must* be more money! There *must* be more money!'

It came whispering from the springs of the still-swaying rocking-horse, and even the horse, bending his wooden, champing head, heard it. The big doll, sitting so pink and smirking in her new pram, could hear it quite plainly, and seemed to be smirking all the more self-consciously because of it. The foolish puppy, too, that took the place of the teddy-bear, he was looking so extraordinarily foolish for no other reason but that he heard the secret whisper all over the house: 'There *must* be more money!'

Yet nobody ever said it aloud. The whisper was everywhere, and therefore no-one spoke it. Just as no-one ever says 'We are breathing!' in spite of the fact that breath is coming and going all the time.

'Mother,' said the boy Paul one day, 'why don't we keep a car of our own? Why do we always use uncle's, or else a taxi?'

'Because we're the poor members of the family,' said the mother.

'But why are we, mother?'

'Well—I suppose,' she said slowly and bitterly, 'it's because your father has no luck.'

The boy was silent for some time.

'Is luck money, mother?' he asked, rather timidly.

'No, Paul. Not quite. It's what causes you to have money.'

'Oh!' said Paul vaguely. 'I thought when Uncle Oscar said filthy lucker, it meant money.'

'Filthy lucre does mean money,' said the mother. 'But it's lucre, not luck.'

'Oh!' said the boy. 'Then what *is* luck, mother?'

'It's what causes you to have money. If you're lucky you have money. That's why it's better to be born lucky than rich. If you're rich, you may lose your money. But if you're lucky, you will always get more money.'

'Oh! Will you? And is father not lucky?'

'Very unlucky, I should say,' she said bitterly.

The boy watched her with unsure eyes.

'Why?' he asked.

'I don't know. Nobody ever knows why one person is lucky and another unlucky.'

'Don't they? Nobody at all? Does *nobody* know?'

'Perhaps God. But He never tells.'

'He ought to, then. And aren't you lucky either, mother?'

'I can't be, if I married an unlucky husband.'

'But by yourself, aren't you?'

'I used to think I was, before I married. Now I think I am very unlucky indeed.'

'Why?'

'Well—never mind! Perhaps I'm not really,' she said.

The child looked at her to see if she meant it. But he saw, by the lines of her mouth, that she was only trying to hide something from him.

'Well, anyhow,' he said stoutly, 'I'm a lucky person.'

'Why?' said his mother, with a sudden laugh.

He stared at her. He didn't even know why he had said it.

'God told me,' he asserted, brazening it out.

'I hope He did, dear!' she said, again with a laugh, but rather bitter.

'He did, mother!'

'Excellent!' said the mother, using one of her husband's exclamations.

The boy saw she did not believe him; or rather, that she paid no attention to his assertion. This angered him somewhere, and made him want to compel her attention.

He went off by himself, vaguely, in a childish way, seeking for the clue to 'luck'. Absorbed, taking no heed of other people, he went about with a sort of stealth, seeking inwardly for luck.

He wanted luck, he wanted it, he wanted it. When the two girls were playing dolls in the nursery, he would sit on his big rocking-horse, charging madly into space, with a frenzy that made the little girls peer at him uneasily. Wildly the horse careered, the waving dark hair of the boy tossed, his eyes had a strange glare in them. The little girls dared not speak to him.

When he had ridden to the end of his mad little journey, he climbed down and stood in front of his rocking-horse, staring fixedly into its lowered face. Its red mouth was slightly open, its big eyes were wide and glassy-bright.

'Now!' he would silently command the snorting steed. 'Now, take me to where there is luck! Now take me!'

And he would slash the horse on the neck with the little whip he had asked Uncle Oscar for. He knew the horse could take him to where there was luck, if only he forced it. So he would mount again and start on his furious ride, hoping at last to get there. He knew he could get there.

'You'll break your horse, Paul!' said the nurse.

'He's always riding like that! I wish he'd leave off!' said his elder sister Joan.

But he only glared down on them in silence. Nurse gave him up. She could make nothing of him. Anyhow, he was growing beyond her.

One day his mother and his Uncle Oscar came in when he was on one of his furious rides. He did not speak to them.

'Hallo, you young jockey! Riding a winner?' said his uncle.

'Aren't you growing too big for a rocking-horse? You're not a very little boy any longer, you know,' said his mother.

But Paul only gave a blue glare from his big, rather close-set eyes. He would speak to nobody when he was in full tilt. His mother watched him with an anxious expression on her face.

At last he suddenly stopped forcing his horse into the mechanical gallop and slid down.

'Well, I got there!' he announced fiercely, his blue eyes still flaring, and his sturdy long legs straddling apart.

'Where did you get to?' asked his mother.

'Where I wanted to go,' he flared back at her.

'That's right, son!' said Uncle Oscar. 'Don't you stop till you get there. What's the horse's name?'

'He doesn't have a name,' said the boy.

'Gets on without all right?' asked the uncle.

'Well, he has different names. He was called Sansovino last week.'

'Sansovino, eh? Won the Ascot. How did you know this name?'

'He always talks about horse-races with Basset,' said Joan.

The uncle was delighted to find that his small nephew was posted with all the racing news. Bassett, the young gardener, who had been wounded in the left foot in the war and had got his present job through Oscar Cresswell, whose batman he had been, was a perfect blade of the 'turf'. He lived in the racing events, and the small boy lived with him.

Oscar Cresswell got it all from Bassett.

'Master Paul comes and asks me, so I can't do more than tell him, sir,' said Bassett, his face terribly serious, as if he were speaking of religious matters.

'And does he ever put anything on a horse he fancies?'

'Well—I don't want to give him away—he's a young sport, a fine sport, sir. Would you mind asking him yourself? He sort of takes a pleasure in it, and perhaps he'd feel I was giving him away, sir, if you don't mind.'

Bassett was serious as a church.

The uncle went back to his nephew and took him off for a ride in the car.

'Say, Paul, old man, do you ever put anything on a horse?' the uncle asked.

The boy watched the handsome man closely.

'Why, do you think I oughtn't to?' he parried.

'Not a bit of it! I thought perhaps you might give me a tip for the Lincoln.'

The car sped on into the country, going down to Uncle Oscar's place in Hampshire.

'Honour bright—' said the nephew.

'Honour bright, son!' said the uncle.

'Well, then, Daffodil.'

'Daffodil! I doubt it, sonny. What about Mirza?'

'I only know the winner,' said the boy. 'That's Daffodil.'

'Daffodil, eh?'

There was a pause. Daffodil was an obscure horse comparatively.

'Uncle!'

'Yes, son?'

'You won't let it go any further, will you? I promised Bassett.'

'Bassett be damned, old man! What's he got to do with it?'

'We're partners. We've been partners from the first. Uncle, he lent me my first five shillings, which I lost. I promised him, honour bright, it was only between me and him; only you gave me that ten-shilling note I started winning with, so I thought you were lucky. You won't let it go any further, will you?'

The boy gazed at his uncle from those big, hot, blue eyes set rather close together. The uncle stirred and laughed uneasily.

'Right you are, son! I'll keep your tip private. Daffodil, eh? How much are you putting on him?'

'All except twenty pounds,' said the boy. 'I keep that in reserve.'

The uncle thought it a good joke.

'You keep twenty pounds in reserve, do you, you young romancer? What are you betting, then?'

'I'm betting three hundred,' said the boy gravely. 'But it's between you and me, Uncle Oscar! Honour bright?'

The uncle burst into a roar of laughter.

'It's between you and me all right, you young Nat Gould,' he said laughing. 'But where's your three hundred?'

'Bassett keeps it for me. We're partners.'

'You are, are you! And what is Bassett putting on Daffodil?'

'He won't go quite as high as I do, I expect. Perhaps he'll go a hundred and fifty.'

'What, pennies?' laughed the uncle.

'Pounds,' said the child, with a surprised look at his uncle. 'Bassett keeps a bigger reserve than I do.'

Between wonder and amusement Uncle Oscar was silent. He pursued the matter no further, but he determined to take his nephew with him to the Lincoln races.

'Now, son,' he said, 'I'm putting twenty on Mirza, and I'll put five on for you on any horse you fancy. What's your pick?'

'Daffodil, uncle.'

'No, not the fiver on Daffodil!'

'I should if it was my own fiver,' said the child.

'Good! Good! Right you are! A fiver for me and a fiver for
you on Daffodil.'

The child had never been to a race-meeting before, and his
eyes were blue fire. He pursed his mouth tight and watched.
A Frenchman just in front had put his money on Lancelot.
Wild with excitement, he flayed his arms up and down, yelling
'Lancelot! Lancelot!' in his French accent.

Daffodil came in first, Lancelot second, Mirza third. The
child, flushed and with eyes blazing, was curiously serene. His
uncle brought him four five-pound notes, four to one.

'What I am to do with these?' he cried, waving them before
the boy's eyes.

'I suppose we'll talk to Bassett,' said the boy. 'I expect I
have fifteen hundred now; and twenty in reserve; and this
twenty.'

His uncle studied him for some moments.

'Look here, son!' he said. 'You're not serious about Bassett
and that fifteen hundred, are you?'

'Yes, I am. But it's between you and me, uncle. Honour
bright?'

'Honour bright all right, son! But I must talk to Bassett.'

'If you'd like to be a partner, uncle, with Bassett and me, we
could all be partners. Only, you'd have to promise, honour
bright, uncle, not to let it go beyond us three. Bassett and I
are lucky, and you must be lucky, because it was your ten
shillings I started winning with. . . .'

Uncle Oscar took both Bassett and Paul into Richmond Park
for an afternoon, and there they talked.

'It's like this, you see, sir,' Bassett said. 'Master Paul would
get me talking about racing events, spinning yarns, you know,
sir. And he was always keen on knowing if I'd made or if I'd
lost. It's about a year since, now, that I put five shillings on
Blush of Dawn for him: and we lost. Then the luck turned, with
that ten shillings he had from you: that we put on Singhalese.
And since that time, it's been pretty steady, all things considering. What do you say, Master Paul?'

'We're all right when we're sure,' said Paul. 'It's when we're
not quite sure that we go down.'

'Oh, but we're careful then,' said Bassett.

'But when are you sure?' smiled Uncle Oscar.

67

'It's Master Paul, sir,' said Bassett in a secret, religious voice. 'It's as if he had it from heaven. Like Daffodil, now, for the Lincoln. That was as sure as eggs.'

'Did you put anything on Daffodil?' asked Oscar Cresswell.

'Yes, sir. I made my bit.'

'And my nephew?'

Bassett was obstinately silent, looking at Paul.

'I made twelve hundred, didn't I, Bassett? I told uncle I was putting three hundred on Daffodil.'

'That's right,' said Bassett, nodding.

'But where's the money?' asked the uncle.

'I keep it safe locked up, sir. Master Paul he can have it any minute he likes to ask for it.'

'What, fifteen hundred pounds?'

'And twenty! And forty, that is, with the twenty he made on the course.'

'It's amazing!' said the uncle.

'If Master Paul offers you to be partners, sir, I would if I were you: if you'll excuse me,' said Bassett.

Oscar Cresswell thought about it.

'I'll see the money,' he said.

They drove home again, and, sure enough, Bassett came round to the garden-house with fifteen hundred pounds in notes. The twenty pounds reserve was left with Joe Glee, in the Turf Commission deposit.

'You see, it's all right, uncle, when I'm sure! Then we go strong, for all we're worth. Don't we, Bassett?'

'We do that, Master Paul.'

'And when are you sure?' said the uncle, laughing.

'Oh, well, sometimes I'm *absolutely* sure, like about Daffodil,' said the boy; 'and sometimes I have an idea; and sometimes I haven't even an idea, have I, Bassett? Then we're careful, because we mostly go down.'

'You do, do you! And when you're sure, like about Daffodil, what makes you sure, sonny?'

'Oh, well, I don't know,' said the boy uneasily. 'I'm sure, you know, uncle; that's all.'

'It's as if he had it from heaven, sir,' Bassett reiterated.

'I should say so!' said the uncle.

But he became a partner. And when the Leger was coming

on Paul was 'sure' about Lively Spark, which was a quite inconsiderable horse. The boy insisted on putting a thousand on the horse. Bassett went for five hundred, and Oscar Cresswell two hundred. Lively Spark came in first, and the betting had been ten to one against him. Paul had made ten thousand.

'You see,' he said, 'I was absolutely sure of him.'

Even Oscar Cresswell had cleared two thousand.

'Look here, son,' he said, 'this sort of thing makes me nervous.'

'It needn't, uncle! Perhaps I shan't be sure again for a long time.'

'But what are you going to do with your money?' asked the uncle.

'Of course,' said the boy, 'I started it for mother. She said she had no luck, because father is unlucky, so I thought if I was lucky, it might stop whispering.'

'What might stop whispering?'

'Our house. I hate our house for whispering.'

'What does it whisper?'

'Why—why'—the boy fidgeted—'why, I don't know. But it's always short of money, you know, uncle.'

'I know it, son, I know it.'

'You know people send mother writs, don't you uncle?'

'I'm afraid I do,' said the uncle.

'And then the house whispers, like people laughing at you behind your back. It's awful, that is! I thought if I was lucky—'

'You might stop it,' added the uncle.

The boy watched him with big blue eyes that had an uncanny cold fire in them, and he said never a word.

'Well, then!' said the uncle. 'What are we doing?'

'I shouldn't like mother to know I was lucky,' said the boy.

'Why not, son?'

'She'd stop me.'

'I don't think she would.'

'Oh!'—and the boy writhed in an odd way—'I don't want her to know, uncle.'

'All right, son! We'll manage it without her knowing.'

They managed it very easily. Paul, at the other's suggestion handed over five thousand pounds to his uncle, who deposited it with the family lawyer, who was then to inform Paul's mother that a relative had put five thousand pounds into his hands, which sum was to be paid out a thousand pounds at a time, on the mother's birthday, for the next five years.

'So she'll have a birthday present of a thousand pounds for five successive years,' said Uncle Oscar. 'I hope it won't make it all the harder for her later.'

Paul's mother had her birthday in November. The house had been 'whispering' worse than ever lately, and, even in spite of his luck, Paul could not bear up against it. He was very anxious to see the effect of the birthday letter, telling his mother about the thousand pounds.

When there were no visitors, Paul now took his meals with his parents, as he was beyond the nursery control. His mother went into town nearly every day. She had discovered that she had an odd knack of sketching furs and dress materials, so she worked secretly in the studio of a friend who was the chief 'artist' for the leading drapers. She drew the figures of ladies in furs and ladies in silk and sequins for the newspaper advertisements. This young woman artist earned several thousand pounds a year, but Paul's mother only made several hundreds, and she was again dissatisfied. She so wanted to be first in something, and she did not succeed, even in making sketches for drapery advertisements.

She was down to breakfast on the morning of her birthday. Paul watched her face as she read her letters. He knew the lawyer's letter. As his mother read it, her face hardened and became more expressionless. Then a cold, determined look came on her mouth. She hid the letter under the pile of others, and said not a word about it.

'Didn't you have anything nice in the post for your birthday, mother?' said Paul.

'Quite moderately nice,' she said, her voice cold and absent.

She went away to town without saying more.

But in the afternoon, Uncle Oscar appeared. He said Paul's mother had had a long interview with the lawyer, asking if the whole five thousand could not be advanced at once, as she was in debt.

'What do you think, uncle?' said the boy.

'I leave it to you, son.'

'Oh, let her have it, then! We can get some more with the other,' said the boy.

'A bird in the hand is worth two in the bush, laddie!' said Uncle Oscar.

'But I'm sure to know for the Grand National; or the Lincolnshire; or else the Derby. I'm sure to know for one of them,' said Paul.

So Uncle Oscar signed the agreement, and Paul's mother touched the whole five thousand. Then something very curious happened. The voices in the house suddenly went mad, like a chorus of frogs on a spring evening. There were certain new furnishings, and Paul had a tutor. He was *really* going to Eton, his father's school, in the following autumn. There were flowers in the winter, and a blossoming of the luxury Paul's mother had been used to. And yet the voices in the house, behind the sprays of mimosa and almond-blossom, and from under the piles of iridescent cushions, simply trilled and screamed in a sort of ecstasy: 'There *must* be more money! Oh-h-h; there *must* be more money. Oh, now, now-w! Now-w-w —there *must* be more money!—more than ever! More than ever!'

It frightened Paul terribly. He studied away at his Latin and Greek with his tutor. But his intense hours were spent with Bassett. The Grand National had gone by: he had not 'known', and had lost a hundred pounds. Summer was at hand. He was in agony for the Lincoln. But even for the Lincoln he didn't 'know', and he lost fifty pounds. He became wild-eyed and strange, as if something were going to explode in him.

'Let it alone, son! Don't you bother about it!' urged Uncle Oscar. But it was as if the boy couldn't really hear what his uncle was saying.

'I've got to know for the Derby! I've got to know for the Derby!' the child reiterated, his big blue eyes blazing with a sort of madness.

His mother noticed how overwrought he was.

'You'd better go to the seaside. Wouldn't you like to go now to the seaside, instead of waiting? I think you'd better,' she said, looking down at him anxiously, her heart curiously heavy because of him.

But the child lifted his uncanny blue eyes.

'I couldn't possibly go before the Derby, mother!' he said, 'I couldn't possibly!'

'Why not?' she said, her voice becoming heavy when she was opposed. 'Why not? You can still go from the seaside to see the Derby with your Uncle Oscar, if that's what you wish. No need for you to wait here. Besides, I think you care too much about these races. It's a bad sign. My family has been a gambling family, and you won't know till you grow up how much damage it has done. But it has done damage. I shall have to send Bassett away, and ask Uncle Oscar not to talk racing to you, unless you promise to be reasonable about it: go away to the seaside and forget it. You're all nerves!'

'I'll do what you like, mother, so long as you don't send me away till after the Derby,' the boy said.

'Send you away from where? Just from this house?'

'Yes,' he said, gazing at her.

'Why, you curious child, what makes you care about this house so much, suddenly? I never knew you loved it.'

He gazed at her without speaking. He had a secret within a secret, something he had not divulged, even to Bassett or to his Uncle Oscar.

But his mother, after standing undecided and a little bit sullen for some moments, said:

'Very well, then! Don't go to the seaside till after the Derby, if you don't wish it. But promise me you won't let your nerves go to pieces. Promise you won't think so much about horse-racing and events, as you call them!'

'Oh no,' said the boy casually. 'I won't think much about them mother, you needn't worry. I wouldn't worry, mother, if I were you.'

'If you were me and I were you,' said his mother, 'I wonder what we should do!'

'But you know you needn't worry, mother, don't you?' the boy repeated.

'I should be awfully glad to know it,' she said wearily.

'Oh, well, you *can*, you know. I mean, you *ought* to know you needn't worry,' he insisted.

'Ought I? Then I'll see about it,' she said.

Paul's secret of secrets was his wooden horse, that which had no name. Since he was emancipated from a nurse and a nursery-governess, he had had his rocking-horse removed to his own bedroom at the top of the house.

'Surely you're too big for a rocking-horse!' his mother had remonstrated.

'Well, you see mother, till I can have a *real* horse, I like to have some sort of animal about,' had been his quaint answer.

'Do you feel he keeps you company?' she laughed.

'Oh yes! He's very good, he always keeps me company, when I'm there,' said Paul.

So the horse, rather shabby, stood in an arrested prance in the boy's bedroom.

The Derby was drawing near, and the boy grew more and more tense. He hardly heard what was spoken to him, he was very frail, and his eyes were really uncanny. His mother had sudden strange seizures of uneasiness about him. Sometimes, for half an hour, she would feel a sudden anxiety about him that was almost anguish. She wanted to rush to him at once, and know he was safe.

Two nights before the Derby, she was at a big party in town, when one of her rushes of anxiety about her boy, her first-born, gripped her heart till she could hardly speak. She fought with the feeling, might and main, for she believed in common sense. But it was too strong. She had to leave the dance and go downstairs to telephone to the country. The children's nursery governess was terribly surprised and startled at being rung up in the night.

'Are the children all right, Miss Wilmot?'

'Oh yes, they are quite all right.'

'Master Paul? Is he all right?'

'He went to bed as right as a trivet. Shall I run up and look at him?'

'No,' said Paul's mother reluctantly. 'No! Don't trouble. It's all right. Don't sit up. We shall be home fairly soon.' She did not want her son's privacy intruded upon.

'Very good,' said the governess.

It was about one o'clock when Paul's mother and father drove up to their house. All was still. Paul's mother went to her room and slipped off her white fur cloak. She had told her maid not to wait up for her. She heard her husband downstairs, mixing a whisky and soda.

And then, because of the strange anxiety at her heart, she stole upstairs to her son's room. Noiselessly she went along the upper corridor. Was there a faint noise? What was it?

She stood, with arrested muscles, outside his door, listening. There was a strange, heavy, and yet not loud noise. Her heart stood still. It was a soundless noise, yet rushing and powerful. Something huge, in violent, hushed motion. What was it? What in God's name was it? She ought to know. She felt that she knew the noise. She knew what it was.

Yet she could not place it. She couldn't say what it was. And yet on and on it went, like a madness.

Softly, frozen with anxiety and fear, she turned the door handle.

The room was dark. Yet in the space near the window, she heard and saw something plunging to and fro. She gazed in fear and amazement.

Then suddenly she switched on the light, and saw her son, in his green pyjamas, madly surging on the rocking-horse. The blaze of light suddenly lit him up, as he urged the wooden horse, and lit her up, as she stood, blonde, in her dress of pale green and crystal, in the doorway.

'Paul!' she cried. 'Whatever are you doing?'

'It's Malabar!' he screamed in a powerful, strange voice. 'It's Malabar!'

His eyes blazed at her for one strange and senseless second, as he ceased urging his wooden horse. Then he fell with a crash to the ground, and she, all her tormented motherhood flooding upon her, rushed to gather him up.

But he was unconscious, and unconscious he remained, with some brain-fever. He talked and tossed, and his mother sat stonily by his side.

'Malabar! It's Malabar! Bassett, Bassett, I know! It's Malabar!'

So the child cried, trying to get up and urge the rocking-horse that gave him his inspiration.

'What does he mean by Malabar?' asked the heart-frozen mother.

'I don't know,' said the father stonily.

'What does he mean by Malabar?' she asked her brother Oscar.

74

'It's one of the horses running for the Derby,' was the answer.

And, in spite of himself, Oscar Cresswell spoke to Bassett, and himself put a thousand on Malabar: at fourteen to one.

The third day of the illness was critical: they were waiting for a change. The boy, with his rather long, curly hair, was tossing ceaselessly on the pillow. He neither slept nor regained consciousness and his eyes were like blue stones. His mother sat, feeling her heart had gone, turned actually into a stone.

In the evening, Oscar Cresswell did not come, but Bassett sent a message, saying could he come up for one moment, just one moment? Paul's mother was very angry at the intrusion, but on second thoughts she agreed. The boy was the same. Perhaps Bassett might bring him to consciousness.

The gardener, a shortish fellow, with a little brown moustache and sharp little brown eyes, tiptoed into the room, touched his imaginary cap to Paul's mother, and stole to the bedside, staring with glittering, smallish eyes at the tossing, dying child.

'Master Paul!' he whispered. 'Master Paul! Malabar came in first all right, a clean win, I did as you told me. You've made over seventy thousand pounds, you have; you've got over eighty thousand. Malabar came in all right, Master Paul.'

'Malabar! Malabar! Did I say Malabar, mother? Did I say Malabar? Do you think I'm lucky, mother? I knew Malabar, didn't I? Over eighty thousand pounds! I call that lucky, don't you mother? Over eighty thousand pounds! I knew, didn't I know I knew? Malabar came in all right. If I ride my horse till I'm sure, then I tell you, Bassett, you can go as high as you like. Did you go for all you were worth, Bassett?'

'I went a thousand on it, Master Paul.'

'I never told you, mother, that if I can ride my horse and get there, then I'm absolutely sure—oh, absolutely! Mother, did I ever tell you? I *am* lucky!'

'No, you never did,' said his mother.

But the boy died in the night.

And even as he lay dead, his mother heard her brother's voice saying to her: 'My God, Hester, you're eighty-odd thousand to the good, and a poor devil of a son to the bad. But, poor devil, poor devil, he's best gone out of a life where he rides his rocking-horse to find a winner.'

Mr Kaplan's White Banner

by Leo Rosten

It was only logical that, having drilled the class before the holidays on the writing of personal letters, Mr Parkhill should now take up the business form with the beginner's grade. Business letters, indeed, might be even more practical from the students' point of view. They might want to apply for a job, or answer an advertisement, or things of that sort.

'The general structure of the business letter follows that of the personal letter,' Mr Parkhill had said. 'It, too, requires the address, the date, a salutation, a final greeting or "complimentary close".' Then he had gone on to explain that the business letter was more formal in mood and content; that the address of the person or company to whom you were writing had to be included in the form of the letter itself, on the left-hand side, above the salutation; that both the salutation and final greeting were formalized: 'Dear Sir,' 'Dear Sirs,' or 'Gentlemen,' and 'Yours truly,' 'Yours very truly,' 'Very truly yours'. Mr Parkhill was a conscientious teacher and, aware of the queer things some of the students had done with previous exercises, he was careful to introduce the beginners' grade to business letters with particular care.

All had gone well—very well. So much had Mr Parkhill been pleased by his success that, for homework, he had assigned a composition entitled 'A Short Business Letter'.

And now the students were presenting their homework on the blackboard for class analysis. Mrs Tomasic, anticipating some halcyon day in the future, was applying for a position as private secretary to the President of the Good English Club. Mr George Weinstein was ordering 'a dozen assorted colours sox size 12 silk' from a well-known department store. Mr Norman Bloom, ever the soul of business, was inscribing a polite but firm note reminding 'S. Levin—Inc.—Jobbers' that they still owed him $17.75 for merchandise taken 'on assignment'. Miss Schneiderman described a hat, coat, and 'pair gloffs' she wished delivered 'C.O.T.'. Mr Hyman Kaplan was copying his letter on the blackboard in the right-hand corner of the room, near the door. There was a serenity in Mr Kaplan's ubiquitous smile as he put the finishing touches to his creation. This night there was something luminous about that smile. Mr Parkhill, always uneasy about the form Mr Kaplan's genius might give to any assignment, found himself reading Mr Kaplan's letter with unconscious curiosity and quite conscious anxiety. This was the letter Mr Kaplan had written:

Bus. Let.

459 E.3. Street
New York
Janu. 8

JOSEPH MANDELBAUM
A-1 Furniture Comp. N.Y.

DEAR SIR MANDELBAUM—

Sarah and me want to buy refrigimator. Sarah wants bad. Always she is saying 'Hymie, the eyes-box is terrible. Leeking.' Is true. So I answer 'Sarah, by me is O.K. refrigimator.'

Because you are in furniture so I'm writing about. How much will cost refrigimator? Is axpensif, maybe by you is more cheap a little. But it *must not* have short circus. If your eye falls on a bargain please pick it up.

Very Truly Your Customer

H*Y*M*A*N K*A*P*L*A*N
(Address on Top)

Best regards Sarah and me.

Affectionately,
H*Y*M*I*E

Mr Parkhill frowned several times during his reading of this document, sighed when he had finished his examination of it, and resigned himself to another tortuous excursion into the strange linguistic universe of his most remarkable student. As for Mr Kaplan, he re-read his handiwork several times lovingly, his eyes half-closed in what was supposed to be a self-critical attitude. He kept shaking his head happily as he read, smiling, as if delighted by the miracle of what he had brought into being. Mr Kaplan was an appreciative soul.

When the last student had finished, Mr Parkhill said quickly, 'I think we'll take your composition *first*, Mr Kaplan.' He wasn't quite sure why he had said that. Generally he started with the exercise in the *left*-hand corner of the blackboard.

'Me *foist*?' asked Mr Kaplan.

'Er—yes.' Mr Parkhill almost wavered at the last minute.

Mr Kaplan's smile widened. 'My!' he said, getting up from his seat. 'Is awreddy *foist* I'm makink rasitations!' By the time he reached the blackboard his smile had become positively celestial.

Mr Kaplan faced the class, as if it were an exercise in Recitation and Speech rather than composition.

'Ladies an' gantleman,' he began, 'in dis lasson I falt a fonny kind problem. A problem abot how—'

'Er—Mr Kaplan,' Mr Parkhill broke in, 'please *read* your letter.'

Only Mr Kaplan's delight in being first carried him over this cruel frustration. 'Podden me,' he said softly. He began to read the letter. ' "Dear Sir Mendelbum." ' He read slowly, with dignity, with feeling. His smile struggled between pride and modesty. When he came to the last words, there was a tinge of melancholy in his voice. ' "Affectionately, Hymie." ' Mr Kaplan sighed. 'Dat's de and.'

'Mr Kaplan,' began Mr Parkhill cautiously, 'do you think that's strictly a *business* letter?'

Mr Kaplan considered this challenge by closing his eyes and whispering to himself. 'Business ladder? *Streectly* business ladder? Is?'

Mr Parkhill waited. The years had taught Mr Parkhill patience.

'It's *abot* business,' suggested Mr Kaplan tentatively.

Mr Parkhill shook his head. 'But the content, Mr Kaplan. The tone. The final—er—well—' Mr Parkhill caught *himself* on the verge of an oration. 'I'll let the class begin the corrections. There are *many* mistakes, Mr Kaplan.'

Mr Kaplan's grave nod indicated that even the wisest of men knew what it was to err.

'Corrections, class. First, let us consider the basic question. Is this a business letter?'

The hand of Rose Mitnick went up with a menacing resolution. When the work of Mr Kaplan was under consideration, Miss Mitnick functioned with devastating efficiency.

'I think this isn't,' she said. 'Because in business letter you don't tell your wife's *first* name. And you don't send "best regards". All that's for *personal* letters like we had before.'

'An' vat if I vanted to wride a *poisonal* business ladder?' asked Mr Kaplan with diabolic logic.

Miss Mitnick paid no attention to this casuistry. 'It's wrong to give family facts in business letter,' she insisted. 'It's no business from the company what is a wife saying to a husband.'

'Aha!' cried Mr Kaplan. 'Mitnick, you too axcited. You forgeddink to *who* is dis ladder!'

Mr Parkhill cleared his throat. 'Er—Mr Kaplan, Miss Mitnick is quite right. One doesn't discuss personal or family details, or give one's wife's first name, in a business letter— which is, after all, to a stranger.'

Mr Kaplan waited until the last echo of Mr Parkhill's voice had died away. Then, when the classroom was very quiet, he spoke. 'Mendelbum,' he said, 'is mine oncle.'

There was a collective gasp. Miss Mitnick flushed. Mr Marcus's eyes opened very wide. Mrs Friedman blinked blankly.

'But Mr Kaplan,' said Mr Parkhill quickly, realizing that in such a mood there were no limits to Mr Kaplan's audacity, 'if the letter *is* addressed to your uncle'—he pronounced 'uncle' suspiciously, but Mr Kaplan's firm nod convinced him that there was no subterfuge here—'then it shouldn't be a business letter in the first place!'

To this Miss Mitnick nodded, with hope.

'Dat pozzled me, too,' said Mr Kaplan graciously. 'An' dat's vy I vas goink to axplain abot de fonny kind problem I falt, in de few voids before I rad de ladder.' His tone was one of righteousness. 'I figgered: buyink a refrigima—'

'Refrig*erator*! "R" not "m".'

'Buyink a refrig*erator* is business. Also de axercise you givink for homevork is abot business. So I must kipp in business *atmosvere*. So in de foist pot I wrote mine oncle a real business ladder—cold, formmal. You know, stock-op!' Mr Kaplan wrinkled his nose into a pictorialization of 'stock-op'. 'But den, by de and, I falt is awreddy time to have mit family fillink. Becawss *is*, efter all, mine oncle. So I put don "Affectionately, Hymie".'

'And is "Affectionately" right for a business letter?' asked Miss Mitnick, trying to conceal the triumph in her voice.

'It's *spalled* right!' Mr Kaplan cried with feeling.

Mr Parkhill felt old and weary; he began to realize the heights yet to be scaled. 'Mr Kaplan,' he said softly, 'we are not concerned with the spelling of "affectionately" at the moment. "Affectionately" is *not* proper in a business letter, nor is "very truly yours" in a personal letter.' He spent a few minutes analysing the impasse. 'You cannot combine the two forms, Mr Kaplan. Either you write a business letter *or* a personal letter.' He suggested that in the future Mr Kaplan write personal letters to his uncle, but choose absolute strangers for his business communications. 'Let us go on with the corrections, please.'

Mr Bloom's hand went up.

'Mistakes is terrible,' he said. 'Where's the address from the company? How is abbreviated "Company"? Where's colon or comma after "Dear Sir"? And "Dear Sir Mandelbaum"! What kind combination is this? Is maybe Mr Kaplan's uncle in English House Lords?'

Mr Kaplan smiled bravely through this fusillade. Even the sarcasm about his titled lineage did no perceptible damage to that smile.

' "Sarah and me" should be "Sarah and I",' Mr Bloom went on. 'And "eyes-box"! Phooey! I-c-e means "ice"; e-y-e-s means "eyes". One is for seeing, the other for freezing!'

Mr Bloom was in faultless form. The class listened breathlessly to his dissection of Mr Kaplan's business letter. His recitation filled them with confidence. When he finished, a forest of hands went up. With new courage the beginner's grade leapt into the critical fray. It was pointed out that 'leaking' was spelled wrong, and 'expensive'. Mr Pinksy remarked pointedly that there should be no capitals after 'Very' in 'Very truly' and cast doubts on the legitimacy of 'Very Truly Your Customer'. Miss Caravello suggested that Mr Mandelbaum might be wise enough to read Mr Kaplan's address without being told where to look for it, in the phrase 'Address on Top'. Even Mrs Moskowitz, simple, uninspired Mrs Moskowitz, added her bit to the autopsy.

'I only know vun ting,' she said. 'I know vat is a circus.

Dat's mit hanimals, clons, tricks, horses. An' you ken't put a circus in icebox—even a "*short* circus"!'

'You don' know abot laktric!' cried Mr Kaplan, desperate to strike back at this united front. 'Ufcawss, you a voman.'

'Laktric—gas—even *candles*!' retorted Mrs Moskowitz. 'Circus ken't go in icebox!'

'Maybe de kind *you* minn,' said Mr Kaplan hotly. 'But in laktricity is alvays denger havink short coicus. Becawss—'

Mr Parkhill intervened, conscious that here was the making of a feud to take its place beside the Mitnick–Kaplan *affaire*. 'You don't mean "short circus", Mr Kaplan. You mean "short cir*cuit*"! C-i-r-c-u-i-t.'

From the expression on Mr Kaplan's face it was clear that even this approximation to 'circus' was a victory for him and a rebuff to Mrs Moskowitz and the forces she had, for the moment, led into battle.

'Another mistake,' said Miss Mitnick suddenly. There was a glow in her cheeks; evidently Miss Mitnick had discovered something very important. Mr Kaplan's eyes turned to narrow slits. 'In the letter is: "If your eye falls on a bargain please pick it up." ' Miss Mitnick read the sentence slowly. ' "If your *eye* falls on a bargain pick *it* up"?'

The class burst into laughter. It was a masterly stroke. Everyone laughed. Even Mr Parkhill, feeling a bit sorry for Mr Kaplan permitted himself a dignified smile.

And suddenly Mr Kaplan joined in the merriment. He didn't laugh; he merely smiled. But his smile was grandiose, invincible, cosmic.

'An' vat's wronk dere, plizz?' he asked, his tone the epitome of confidence.

Mr Bloom should have known that he was treading on ground mined with dynamite. But so complete had been the rout of Hyman Kaplan that Mr Bloom threw caution to the winds. 'Miss Mitnick's right! "If your *eye* falls on a bargain please pick *it* up"? Some English, Mr Kaplan!'

Then Mr Kaplan struck.

'Mine oncle,' he said, 'has a gless eye.'

The effect was incredible. The laughter came to a convulsive stop. Mr Bloom's mouth fell open. Miss Mitnick dropped her pencil. Mrs Moskowitz looked at Mr Kaplan as if she had seen a vision; she wondered how she had dared criticize such a man. And Mr Kaplan's smile was that of a child, deep in some lovely and imperishable sleep. He was like a man who had redeemed himself, a man whose honour, unsmirched, was before him like a dazzling white banner.

The Verger by Somerset Maugham

There had been a christening that afternoon at St. Peter's, Neville Square, and Albert Edward Foreman still wore his verger's gown. He kept his new one, its folds as full and stiff as though it were made not of alpaca but of perennial bronze, for funerals and weddings (St. Peter's, Neville Square, was a church much favoured by the fashionable for these ceremonies) and now he wore only his second-best. He wore it with complacency, for it was the dignified symbol of his office, and without it (when he took it off to go home) he had the disconcerting sensation of being somewhat insufficiently clad. He took pains with it; he pressed it and ironed it himself. During the sixteen years he had been verger of this church he had had a succession of such gowns, but he had never been able to throw them away when they were worn out and the complete series, neatly wrapped up in brown paper, lay in the bottom drawers of the wardrobe in his bedroom.

The verger busied himself quietly, replacing the painted wooden cover on the marble font, taking away a chair that had been brought for an infirm old lady, and waited for the vicar to have finished in the vestry so that he could tidy up in there and go home. Presently he saw him walk across the chancel, genuflect in front of the high altar and come down the aisle; but he still wore his cassock.

'What's he 'anging about for?' the verger said to himself. 'Don't 'e know I want my tea?'

The vicar had been but recently appointed, a red-faced energetic man in his early forties, and Albert Edward still regretted his predecessor, a clergyman of the old school who preached leisurely sermons in a silvery voice and dined out a great deal with his more aristocratic parishioners. He liked things in church to be just so, but he never fussed; he was not like this new man who wanted to have his finger in every pie. But Albert Edward was tolerant. St. Peter's was in a very good neighbourhood and the parishioners were a very nice class of people. The new vicar had come from the East End and he couldn't be expected to fall in all at once with the discreet ways of his fashionable congregation.

'All this 'ustle,' said Albert Edward. 'But give 'im time, he'll learn.'

When the vicar had walked down the aisle so far that he could address the verger without raising his voice more than was becoming in a place of worship, he stopped.

'Foreman, will you come into the vestry for a minute. I have something to say to you.'

'Very good, sir.'

The vicar waited for him to come up and they walked up the church together.

'A very nice christening, I thought, sir. Funny 'ow the baby stopped cryin' the moment you took him.'

'I've noticed they very often do,' said the vicar, with a little smile. 'After all, I've had a good deal of practice with them.'

It was a source of subdued pride to him that he could nearly always quiet a whimpering infant by the manner in which he held it and he was not unconscious of the amused admiration with which mothers and nurses watched him settle the baby in the crook of his surpliced arm. The verger knew that it pleased him to be complimented on his talent.

The vicar preceded Albert Edward into the vestry. Albert Edward was a trifle surprised to find the two churchwardens there. He had not seen them come in. They gave him pleasant nods.

'Good afternoon, my lord. Good afternoon, sir,' he said to one after the other.

They were elderly men, both of them, and they had been churchwardens almost as long as Albert Edward had been verger. They were sitting now at a handsome refectory table that the old vicar had brought many years before from Italy and the vicar sat down in the vacant chair between them. Albert Edward faced them, the table between him and them, and wondered with slight uneasiness what was the matter. He remembered still the occasion on which the organist had got into trouble and the bother they had all had to hush things up. In a church like St. Peter's, Neville Square, they couldn't afford a scandal. On the vicar's red face was a look of resolute benignity, but the others bore an expression that was slightly troubled.

'He's been naggin' them, he 'as,' said the verger to himself. 'He's jockeyed them into doin' something, but they don't 'alf like it. That's what it is, you mark my words.'

But his thoughts did not appear on Albert Edward's clean-cut and distinguished features. He stood in a respectful but not obsequious attitude. He had been in service before he was appointed to his ecclesiastical office, but only in very good houses, and his deportment was irreproachable. Starting as a page-boy in the household of a merchant-prince, he had risen by due degrees from the position of fourth to first footman, for a year he had been single-handed butler to a widowed peeress and, till the vacancy occurred at St. Peter's, butler with two men under him in the house of a retired ambassador. He was tall, spare, grave and dignified. He looked, if not like a duke, at least like an actor of the old school who specialized in dukes' parts. He had tact, firmness and self-assurance. His character was unimpeachable.

The vicar began briskly.

'Foreman, we've got something rather unpleasant to say to you. You've been here a great many years and I think his lordship and the general agree with me that you've fulfilled the duties of your office to the satisfaction of everybody concerned.'

The two churchwardens nodded.

'But a most extraordinary circumstance came to my knowledge the other day and I felt it my duty to impart it to the churchwardens. I discovered to my astonishment that you could neither read nor write.'

The verger's face betrayed no sign of embarrassment.

'The last vicar knew that, sir,' he replied. 'He said it didn't make no difference. He always said there was a great deal too much education in the world for 'is taste.'

'It's the most amazing thing I ever heard,' cried the general. 'Do you mean to say that you've been verger of this church for sixteen years and never learned to read or write?'

'I went into service when I was twelve, sir. The cook in the first place tried to teach me once, but I didn't seem to 'ave the knack for it, and then what with one thing and another I never

seemed to 'ave the time. I've never really found the want of it.
I think a lot of these young fellows waste a rare lot of time
readin' when they might be doin' something useful.'

'But don't you want to know the news?' said the other
churchwarden. 'Don't you ever want to write a letter?'

'No, me lord, I seem to manage very well without. And of
late years now they've all these pictures in the papers I get to
know what's goin' on pretty well. Me wife's quite a scholar
and if I want to write a letter she writes it for me. It's not as
if I was a bettin' man.'

The two churchwardens gave the vicar a troubled glance
and then looked down at the table.

'Well, Foreman, I've talked the matter over with these
gentlemen and they quite agree with me that the situation is
impossible. At a church like St. Peter's, Neville Square, we
cannot have a verger who can neither read nor write.'

Albert Edward's thin, sallow face reddened and he moved
uneasily on his feet, but he made no reply.

'Understand me, Foreman, I have no complaint to make
against you. You do your work quite satisfactorily; I have the
highest opinion both of your character and of your capacity;
but we haven't the right to take the risk of some accident that
might happen owing to your lamentable ignorance. It's a
matter of prudence as well as principle.'

'But couldn't you learn, Foreman?' asked the general.

'No, sir, I'm afraid I couldn't, not now. You see, I'm not
as young as I was and if I couldn't seem able to get the letters
in me 'ead when I was a nipper I don't think there's much
chance of it now.'

'We don't want to be harsh with you, Foreman,' said the
vicar. 'But the churchwardens and I have quite made up
our minds. We'll give you three months and if at the end of
that time you cannot read and write, I'm afraid you'll have
to go.'

Albert Edward had never liked the new vicar. He'd said
from the beginning that they'd made a mistake when they
gave him St. Peter's. He wasn't the type of man they wanted
with a classy congregation like that. And now he straightened
himself a little. He knew his value and he wasn't going to
allow himself to be put upon.

'I'm very sorry, sir, I'm afraid it's no good. I'm too old a dog to learn new tricks. I've lived a good many years without knowin' 'ow to read and write, and without wishin' to praise myself, self-praise is no recommendation, I don't mind sayin' I've done my duty in that state of life in which it 'as pleased a merciful providence to place me, and if I *could* learn now I don't know as I'd want to.'

'In that case, Foreman, I'm afraid you must go.'

'Yes, sir, I quite understand. I shall be 'appy to 'and in my resignation as soon as you've found somebody to take my place.'

But when Albert Edward with his usual politeness had closed the church door behind the vicar and the two church-wardens he could not sustain the air of unruffled dignity with which he had borne the blow inflicted upon him and his lips quivered. He walked slowly back to the vestry and hung up on its proper peg his verger's gown. He sighed as he thought of all the grand funerals and smart weddings it had seen. He tidied everything up, put on his coat, and hat in hand walked down the aisle. He locked the church door behind him. He strolled across the square, but deep in his sad thoughts he did not take the street that led him home, where a nice strong cup of tea awaited him; he took the wrong turning. He walked slowly along. His heart was heavy. He did not know what he should do with himself. He did not fancy the notion of going back to domestic service; after being his own master for so many years, for the vicar and churchwardens could say what they liked, it was he that had run St. Peter's, Neville Square, he could scarcely demean himself by accepting a situation. He had saved a tidy sum, but not enough to live on without doing something, and life seemed to cost more every year. He had never thought to be troubled with such questions. The vergers of St. Peter's, like the popes of Rome, were there for life. He had often thought of the pleasant reference the vicar would make in his sermon at evensong the first Sunday after his death to the long and faithful service, and the exemplary character of their late verger, Albert Edward Foreman. He sighed deeply. Albert Edward was a non-smoker and a total abstainer, but with a certain latitude; that is to say he liked a glass of beer with his dinner and when he was tired he enjoyed a cigarette. It occurred to him now that one would comfort him and since he did not carry them he looked about him for a shop where he could buy a packet of Gold Flakes. He did not at once see one and walked on a little. It was a long street, with all sorts of shops in it, but there was not a single one where you could buy cigarettes.

'That's strange,' said Albert Edward.

To make sure, he walked right up the street again. No, there was no doubt about it. He stopped and looked reflectively up and down.

'I can't be the only man as walks along this street and wants a fag,' he said. 'I shouldn't wonder but what a fellow might do very well with a little shop here. Tobacco and sweets, you know.'

He gave a sudden start.

'That's an idea,' he said. 'Strange 'ow things come to you when you least expect it.'

He turned, walked home, and had his tea.

'You're very silent this afternoon, Albert,' his wife remarked.

'I'm thinkin',' he said.

He considered the matter from every point of view and next day he went along the street and by good luck found a little shop to let that looked as though it would exactly suit him. Twenty-four hours later he had taken it and when a month after that he left St. Peter's, Neville Square, for ever, Albert Edward Foreman set up in business as a tobacconist and newsagent. His wife said it was a dreadful come-down after being verger of St. Peter's, but he answered that you had to move with the times, the church wasn't what it was, and 'enceforward he was going to render unto Caesar what was Caesar's. Albert Edward did very well. He did so well that in a year or so it struck him that he might take a second shop and put a manager in. He looked for another long street that hadn't got a tobacconist in it and when he found it, and a shop to let, took it and stocked it. This was a success too. Then it occurred to him that if he could run two he could run half a dozen, so he began walking about London, and whenever he found a long street that had no tobacconist and a shop to let he took it. In the course of ten years he had acquired no less than ten shops and he was making money hand over fist. He went round to all of them himself every Monday, collected the week's takings and took them to the bank.

One morning when he was there paying in a bundle of notes and a heavy bag of silver the cashier told him that the manager would like to see him. He was shown into an office and the manager shook hands with him.

'Mr Foreman, I wanted to have a talk to you about the money you've got on deposit with us. D'you know exactly how much it is?'

'Not within a pound or two, sir; but I've got a pretty rough idea.'

'Apart from what you paid in this morning it's a little over thirty thousand pounds. That's a very large sum to have on deposit, and I should have thought you'd do better to invest it.'

'I wouldn't want to take no risk, sir. I know it's safe in the bank.'

'You needn't have the least anxiety. We'll make you out a list of absolutely gilt-edged securities. They'll bring you in a better rate of interest than we can possibly afford to give you.'

A troubled look settled on Mr Foreman's distinguished face. 'I've never 'ad anything to do with stocks and shares and I'd 'ave to leave it all in your 'ands,' he said.

The manager smiled. 'We'll do everything. All you'll have to do next time you come in is just to sign the transfers.'

'I could do that all right,' said Albert uncertainly. 'But 'ow should I know what I was signin'?'

'I suppose you can read,' said the manager a trifle sharply.

Mr Foreman gave him a disarming smile.

'Well, sir, that's just it. I can't. I know it sounds funny-like, but there it is, I can't read or write, only me name, an' I only learnt to do that when I went into business.

The manager was so surprised that he jumped up from his chair.

'That's the most extraordinary thing I ever heard.'

'You see, it's like this, sir, I never 'ad the opportunity until it was too late and then some'ow I wouldn't. I got obstinate-like.'

The manager stared at him as though he were a prehistoric monster.

'And do you mean to say that you've built up this important

business and amassed a fortune of thirty thousand pounds without being able to read or write? Good God, man, what would you be now if you had been able to?'

'I can tell you that, sir,' said Mr Foreman, a little smile on his still aristocratic features. 'I'd be verger of St. Peter's, Neville Square.'

First Confession *by Frank O'Connor*

All the trouble began when my grandfather died and my grandmother—my father's mother—came to live with us. Relations in the one house are a strain at the best of times, but, to make matters worse, my grandmother was a real old countrywoman and quite unsuited to the life in town. She had a fat, wrinkled old face, and, to Mother's great indignation, went round the house in bare feet—the boots had her crippled, she said. For dinner she had a jug of porter and a pot of potatoes with—sometimes—a bit of salt fish, and she poured out the potatoes on the table and ate them slowly, with great relish, using her fingers by way of a fork.

Now, girls are supposed to be fastidious, but I was the one who suffered most from this. Nora, my sister, just sucked up to the old woman for the penny she got every Friday out of the old-age pension, a thing I could not do. I was too honest, that was my trouble; and when I was playing with Bill Connell, the sergeant-major's son, and saw my grandmother steering up the path with the jug of porter sticking out from beneath her shawl, I was mortified. I made excuses not to let him come into the house, because I could never be sure what she would be up to when we went in.

When Mother was at work and my grandmother made the dinner I wouldn't touch it. Nora once tried to make me, but I hid under the table from her and took the bread-knife with me for protection. Nora let on to be very indignant (she wasn't, of course, but she knew Mother saw through her, so she sided with Gran) and came after me. I lashed out at her with the bread-knife, and after that she left me alone. I stayed there till Mother came in from work and made my dinner, but when Father came in later Nora said in a shocked voice: 'Oh, Dadda, do you know what Jackie did at dinner-time?' Then, of course, it all came out. Father gave me a flaking; Mother interfered; and for days after that he didn't speak to me and Mother barely spoke to Nora. And all because of that old woman! God knows, I was heart-scalded.

Then, to crown my misfortunes, I had to make my first confession and communion. It was an old woman called Ryan who prepared us for these. She was about the one age with Gran; she was well-to-do, lived in a big house on Montenotte, wore a black cloak and bonnet, and came every day to school at three o'clock when we should have been going home, and talked to us of hell. She may have mentioned the other place as well, but that could only have been by accident, for hell had the first place in her heart.

She lit a candle, took out a new half-crown, and offered it to the first boy who would hold one finger—only one finger!—in the flame for five minutes by the school clock. Being always very ambitious I was tempted to volunteer, but I thought it might look greedy. Then she asked were we afraid of holding one finger—only one finger!—in a little candle flame for five minutes and not afraid of burning all over in roasting hot furnaces for all eternity. 'All eternity! Just think of that! A whole lifetime goes by and it's nothing, not even a drop in the ocean of your sufferings.' The woman was really interesting about hell, but my attention was all fixed on the half-crown. At the end of the lesson she put it back in her purse. It was a great disappointment; a religious woman like that, you wouldn't think she'd bother about a thing like a half-crown.

Another day she said she knew a priest who woke one night to find a fellow he didn't recognize leaning over the end of his bed. The priest was a bit frightened—naturally enough—but he asked the fellow what he wanted, and the fellow said in a deep, husky voice that he wanted to go to confession. The priest said it was an awkward time and wouldn't it do in the morning, but the fellow said that last time he went to confession, there was one sin he kept back, being ashamed to mention it, and now it was always on his mind. Then the priest knew it was a bad case, because the fellow was after making a bad confession and committing a mortal sin. He got up to dress, and just then the cock crew in the yard outside, and—lo and behold!—when the priest looked round there was no sign of the fellow, only a smell of burning timber, and when the priest looked at his bed didn't he see the print of two hands burned in it? That was because the fellow had made a bad confession. This story made a shocking impression on me.

But the worst of all was when she showed us how to examine our conscience. Did we take the name of the Lord, our God, in vain? Did we honour our father and our mother? (I asked her did this include grandmothers and she said it did.) Did we love our neighbours as ourselves? Did we covet our neighbour's goods? (I thought of the way I felt about the penny that Nora got every Friday.) I decided that, between one thing and another, I must have broken the whole ten commandments, all on account of that old woman, and so far as I could see, so long as she remained in the house I had no hope of ever doing anything else.

I was scared to death of confession. The day the whole class went I let on to have a toothache, hoping my absence wouldn't be noticed; but at three o'clock, just as I was feeling safe, along comes a chap with a message from Mrs Ryan that I was to go to confession myself on Saturday and be at the chapel for communion with the rest. To make it worse, Mother couldn't come with me and sent Nora instead.

Now, that girl had ways of tormenting me that Mother never knew of. She held my hand as we went down the hill, smiling sadly and saying how sorry she was for me, as if she were bringing me to the hospital for an operation.

'Oh, God help us!' she moaned. 'Isn't it a terrible pity you weren't a good boy? Oh, Jackie, my heart bleeds for you! How will you ever think of all your sins? Don't forget you have to tell him about the time you kicked Gran on the shin.'

'Lemme go!' I said, trying to drag myself free of her. 'I don't want to go to confession at all.'

'But sure, you'll have to go to confession, Jackie,' she replied in the same regretful tone. 'Sure, if you didn't, the parish priest would be up to the house, looking for you. 'Tisn't, God knows, that I'm not sorry for you. Do you remember the time you tried to kill me with the bread-knife under the table? And the language you used to me? I don't know what he'll do with you at all, Jackie. He might have to send you up to the bishop.'

I remember thinking bitterly that she didn't know the half of what I had to tell—if I told it. I knew I couldn't tell it, and understood perfectly why the fellow in Mrs Ryan's story made a bad confession; it seemed to me a great shame that people wouldn't stop criticizing him. I remember that steep hill down to the church, and the sunlit hillsides beyond the valley of the river, which I saw in the gaps between the houses like Adam's last glimpse of Paradise.

Then, when she had manoeuvred me down the long flight of steps to the chapel yard, Nora suddenly changed her tone. She became the raging malicious devil she really was.

'There you are!' she said with a yelp of triumph, hurling me through the church door. 'And I hope he'll give you the penitential psalms, you dirty little caffler.'

I knew then I was lost, given up to eternal justice. The door with the coloured-glass panels swung shut behind me, the sunlight went out and gave place to deep shadow, and the wind whistled outside so that the silence within seemed to crackle like ice under my feet. Nora sat in front of me by the confession box. There were a couple of old women ahead of her, and then a miserable-looking poor devil came and wedged me in at the other side, so that I couldn't escape even if I had the courage. He joined his hands and rolled his eyes in the direction of the roof, muttering aspirations in an anguished tone, and I wondered had he a grandmother too. Only a grandmother could account for a fellow behaving in that heart-broken way, but he was better off than I, for he at least could go and confess his sins, while I would make a bad confession and then die in the night and be continually coming back and burning people's furniture.

Nora's turn came, and I heard the sound of something slamming, and then her voice as if butter wouldn't melt in her mouth, and then another slam, and out she came. God, the hypocrisy of women! Her eyes were lowered, her head was bowed, and her hands were joined very low down on her stomach, and she walked up the aisle to the side altar looking like a saint. You never saw such an exhibition of devotion; and I remembered the devilish malice with which she had tormented me all the way from our door, and wondered were all religious people like that, really. It was my turn now. With the fear of damnation in my soul I went in, and the confessional door closed of itself behind me.

It was pitch-dark and I couldn't see priest or anything else. Then I really began to be frightened. In the darkness it was a matter between God and me, and He had all the odds. He knew what my intentions were before I even started; I had no chance. All I had ever been told about confession got mixed up in my mind, and I knelt to one wall and said: 'Bless me, father, for I have sinned; this is my first confession.' I waited for a few minutes, but nothing happened, so I tried it on the other wall. Nothing happened there either. He had me spotted all right.

It must have been then that I noticed the shelf at about one height with my head. It was really a place for grown-up people to rest their elbows, but in my distracted state I thought it was probably the place you were supposed to kneel. Of course, it was on the high side and not very deep, but I was always good at climbing and managed to get up all right. Staying up was the trouble. There was room only for my knees, and nothing you could get a grip on but a sort of wooden moulding a bit above it. I held on to the moulding and repeated the words a little louder, and this time something happened all right. A slide was slammed back; a little light entered the box, and a man's voice said: 'Who's there?'

''Tis me, father,' I said for fear he mightn't see me and go away again. I couldn't see him at all. The place the voice came from was under the moulding, about level with my knees, so I took a good grip of the moulding and swung myself down till I saw the astonished face of a young priest looking up at me. He had to put his head on one side to see me, and I had to put mine on one side to see him, so we were more or less talking to one another upside-down. It struck me as a queer way of hearing confessions, but I didn't feel it my place to criticize.

'Bless me, father, for I have sinned; this is my first confession,' I rattled off all in one breath, and swung myself down the least shade more to make it easier for him.

'What are you doing up there?' he shouted in an angry voice, and the strain the politeness was putting on my hold of the moulding, and the shock of being addressed in such an uncivil tone, were too much for me. I lost my grip, tumbled, and hit the door an unmerciful wallop before I found myself flat on my back in the middle of the aisle. The people who had been waiting stood up with their mouths open. The priest opened the door of the middle box and came out, pushing his biretta back from his forehead; he looked something terrible. Then Nora came scampering down the aisle.

'Oh, you dirty little caffler!' she said. 'I might have known you'd do it. I might have known you'd disgrace me. I can't leave you out of my sight for one minute.'

Before I could even get to my feet to defend myself she bent down and gave me a clip across the ear. This reminded me that I was so stunned I had even forgotten to cry, so that people might think I wasn't hurt at all, when in fact I was probably maimed for life. I gave a roar out of me.

'What's all this about?' the priest hissed, getting angrier than ever and pushing Nora off me. 'How dare you hit the child like that, you little vixen?'

'But I can't do my penance with him, father,' Nora cried, cocking an outraged eye up at him.

'Well, go and do it, or I'll give you some more to do,' he said, giving me a hand up. 'Was it coming to confession you were, my poor man?' he asked me.

''Twas, father,' said I with a sob.

'Oh,' he said respectfully, 'a big hefty fellow like you must have terrible sins. Is this your first?'

''Tis, father,' said I.

'Worse and worse,' he said gloomily. 'The crimes of a lifetime. I don't know will I get rid of you at all today. You'd better wait now till I'm finished with these old ones. You can see by the looks of them they haven't much to tell.'

'I will, father,' I said with something approaching joy.

The relief of it was really enormous. Nora stuck out her tongue at me from behind his back, but I couldn't even be bothered retorting. I knew from the very moment that man opened his mouth that he was intelligent above the ordinary. When I had time to think, I saw how right I was. It only stood to reason that a fellow confessing after seven years would have more to tell than people that went every week. The crimes of a lifetime, exactly as he said. It was only what he expected, and the rest was the cackle of old women and girls with their talk of hell, the bishop, and the penitential psalms. That was all they knew. I started to make my examination of conscience, and barring the one bad business of my grandmother it didn't seem so bad.

The next time, the priest steered me into the confession box himself and left the shutter back the way I could see him get in and sit down at the further side of the grille from me.

'Well, now,' he said, 'what do they call you?'

'Jackie, father,' said I.

'And what's a-trouble to you, Jackie?'

'Father,' I said, feeling I might as well get it over while I had him in good humour, 'I had it all arranged to kill my grandmother.'

He seemed a bit shaken by that, all right, because he said nothing for quite a while.

'My goodness,' he said at last, 'that'd be a shocking thing to do. What put that into your head?'

'Father,' I said, feeling very sorry for myself, 'she's an awful woman.'

'Is she?' he asked. 'What way is she awful?'

'She takes porter, father,' I said, knowing well from the way Mother talked of it that this was a mortal sin, and hoping it would make the priest take a more favourable view of my case.

'Oh, my!' he said, and I could see he was impressed.

'And snuff, father,' said I.

'That's a bad case, sure enough, Jackie,' he said.

'And she goes round in her bare feet, father,' I went on in a rush of self-pity, 'and she know I don't like her, and she gives pennies to Nora and none to me, and my da sides with her and flakes me, and one night I was so heart-scalded I made up my mind I'd have to kill her.'

'And what would you do with the body?' he asked with great interest.

'I was thinking I could chop that up and carry it away in a barrow I have,' I said.

'Begor, Jackie,' he said, 'do you know you're a terrible child?'

'I know, father,' I said, for I was just thinking the same thing myself. 'I tried to kill Nora too with a bread-knife under the table, only I missed her.'

'Is that the little girl that was beating you just now?' he asked.

''Tis, father.'

'Someone will go for her with a bread-knife one day, and he won't miss her,' he said rather cryptically. 'You must have great courage. Between ourselves, there's a lot of people I'd like to do the same to but I'd never have the nerve. Hanging is an awful death.'

'Is it, father?' I asked with the deepest interest—I was always very keen on hanging. 'Did you ever see a fellow hanged?'

'Dozens of them,' he said solemnly. 'And they all died roaring.'

'Jay!' I said.

'Oh, a horrible death!' he said with great satisfaction. 'Lots of the fellows I saw killed their grandmothers too, but they all said 'twas never worth it.'

He had me there for a full ten minutes talking, and then walked out the chapel yard with me. I was genuinely sorry to part with him, because he was the most entertaining character I'd ever met in the religious line. Outside, after the shadow of the church, the sunlight was like the roaring of waves on a beach; it dazzled me; and when the frozen silence melted and I heard the screech of trams on the road my heart soared. I knew now I wouldn't die in the night and come back, leaving marks on my mother's furniture. It would be a great worry to her, and the poor soul had enough.

Nora was sitting on the railing, waiting for me, and she put on a very sour puss when she saw the priest with me. She was mad jealous because a priest had never come out of the church with her.

'Well,' she asked coldly, after he left me, 'what did he give you?'

'Three Hail Marys,' I said.

'Three Hail Marys,' she repeated incredulously. 'You mustn't have told him anything.'

'I told him everything,' I said confidently.

'About Gran and all?'

'About Gran and all.'

(All she wanted was to be able to go home and say I'd made a bad confession.)

'Did you tell him you went for me with the bread-knife?' she asked with a frown.

'I did to be sure.'

'And he only gave you three Hail Marys?'

'That's all.'

She slowly got down from the railing with a baffled air. Clearly, this was beyond her. As we mounted the steps back to the main road she looked at me suspiciously.

'What are you sucking?' she asked.

'Bullseyes.'

'Was it the priest gave them to you?'

''Twas.'

'Lord, God,' she wailed bitterly, 'some people have all the luck! 'Tis no advantage to anybody trying to be good. I might just as well be a sinner like you.'

The Bottomless Well *by Walter S Terry*

Single file they walked down the rocky trail that he had not travelled in thirty years—not since he was Carol's age. Carol followed a few steps behind him, and Mike, Carol's shadow, placed his tennis-shoed feet deliberately where hers had been.

'How much farther is it, Daddy?' Carol said in the measured tones of her solemn adolescence.

David looked around at her, seeing the brisk movement of her bare legs under a body thinning out but still retaining a residue of little-girl plumpness.

'You tired?'

'I wish I had a horse,' she said.

'Let's rest,' Mike said with his eight-year-old's directness.

The children selected rocks on either side of the trail and sat.

'Horse,' David said. 'Are you still on that horse kick?'

Carol drank from her canteen. 'I'd take care of it,' she said solemnly. 'Feed it.'

'Living on a mountaintop is not the same as living on a farm,' David said. He pulled a flashlight out of one hip pocket and a half-full bottle of beer out of the other. He used his thumb to remove the pressed-back-on-cap. He sat drinking the beer and looking out into the mountain forest. Red and white oaks, hickory and sweet-gum trees provided a lush canopy of June foliage over their heads. The earth smelled dank and musty from a recent rain. *It won't carry me,* he thought. *I should've brought the flask.*

But Grace had been worried-worried-worried, as usual. ('Surely you don't need to drink on a hike with the *children.*') He didn't bother to remind her that his drinking was deliberate, calculated, and always under control when he wanted it to be. (It's no worse than any number of other things that we bribe our senses with in an effort to make life more bearable. Why don't we give them *all* up: coffee, cigarettes, rich foods . . . copulation?)

'We could keep it in the garage in the wintertime,' Carol said. 'When you build it, I mean.'

David glanced sharply at her to see if he could detect any hint of innuendo in the 'when you build it'.

Her face was solemnly inscrutable.

I wouldn't put it past her, he thought.

If he had slowed down in his initially ambitious house-building project it was because every human machine must slow down as it approaches its death. He was on the brink of forty, not a golden thirty-two as he had been when he started the project. He was flat tired; and the spirit of adventure and personal accomplishment in the beginning had given way to a drudgery that he found increasingly difficult to force himself to.

'Horse,' he muttered. 'Carol, every twelve-year-old girl in the world wants a horse. It's tied in with her sexual development.'

'Daddy,' she said evenly, 'I just want a horse.'

'What's "sexy devilment"?' said Mike, chewing a leaf.

David laughed. 'Good paraphrasing, boy.'

'You wouldn't understand,' Carol said quietly.

'I don't,' he replied. 'What's "parapraising"?'

At Flint Arsenal, in the valley and beyond the town, a static test rocket rumbled. David listened, automatically counting off seconds, trying to determine which one it was. The sound ended abruptly.

He shrugged. *Whatever it was it didn't blow up.*

A deep silence enfolded them. Not even the buzz of a cricket was to be heard. The children appeared to be awed by it, cutting their large, children's eyes slowly from side to side as they drank from their canteens.

David arose, shoving the flashlight back into his pocket and pitching the empty beer bottle into a clump of bushes. He belched, wryly twisting his face at the memory of a rebellious stomach. 'We'd better get going if we want to see this hole in the ground.'

They started down the trail again. His mind turned to things he *should* be doing—like installing the kitchen cabinet doors. *Grace has been waiting six years, with her groceries showing. . . Hell, I should be hiking with my daughter and son; I haven't got around to that either. I can't remember the last time, or even if there was a last time. First too busy, then too tired.*

He thought again of the left-behind flask: instant energy;

instant optimism; fountain of youth. He wished fervently for a good stiff optimistic drink of deliberately calculated bourbon.

The trail took a sharp turn to the left, becoming steeper. At the end of the turn Bottomless Well came into view. David saw that there was the remains of a barbed wire fence around the site and, nearby, a small stone house that the CCC had built, so he had heard, back in the 'thirties. There once had been plans to build an access road to the site and make it a public attraction. The plans had for some reason fallen through and only the fading ghosts of human meddling remained.

The opening of the 'well' proper, essentially a vertical-running cave, was at the centre of a large depression in the ground, a sink-hole. There was an old theory that the 'well' extended all the way down through the mountain and connected with great limestone caverns under the town of Garth at the mountain's foot. In support of this theory was the legend of the duck that had been dropped into the hole, reappearing a week later much ruffled but alive out of Garth Spring, which flowed under the town and out at the bottom of the hill on which the town was built.

However, recent exploration by local spelunkers had failed to find the legendary passage and they had drily reported its bottom to be some three hundred feet into the rocky bowels of Buena Vista Mountain.

David extended his arms in warning as they approached the funnel-shaped depression. The walls of the funnel descended at a forty-five-degree angle to the dark opening of the 'well'.

'Take it very easy,' he said. He had forgotten what a treacherous thing this hole in the ground was. The mouth of the crater was roughly circular and perhaps sixty feet across. The 'well' opening at its bottom was more irregular in shape and about twenty feet across at its widest point. Someone had rolled a hickory log across the opening—not too long ago, judging by its sound appearance. David guessed that the log had been a part of the spelunking activity; certainly, without it, it would be hard to imagine what they would have secured a line to. Other evidence of activity at the site was a set of crude dug-out steps leading down the earth bank of the funnel to the near end of the log.

David picked up a small stone and pitched it toward the

opening. After a prolonged silence, there was a faint *clink*, another silence, then another *clink*; after that it was difficult to tell whether you heard anything or not.

'Moses!' Mike whispered. 'It must be a thousand feet deep!'

'Bottomless,' Carol said.

David glanced at her, wondering at the solemnness of this little person he had sired. He could never help suspecting a precocious sardonicness, or at least satire, in her consistently restrained manner and speech.

'The folks who went down there say it's about three hundred feet.' David addressed the remark to Mike. 'Down. Then a short tunnel to the side.'

'The length of a football field,' Carol said, as if to herself.

'I'll take you down,' David said, 'but one at a time. I couldn't watch both of you at once.' He gazed at them, almost selecting Mike first out of spite. 'You first, Carol.'

'All right.'

'Mike,' David said, 'you stand *right there*. Don't you move until we come back up.'

'Yessir.'

They had to duck through the barbed wire to get to the steps leading down. David went first, keeping his body low and back-leaning, insisting that Carol do the same. At the log they stopped and cautiously peered over into the chasm with their hands on the end of the log for support. The walls of the hole, though generally sheer, were broken at irregular intervals by narrow, rounded ledges of stone. The flashlight beam was able to probe only a feeble distance into the darkness. David picked up a pebble and tried to direct it so that it would miss the ledges and free-fall as far as possible. As he let it go he counted 'one-thousand-one, one-thousand-two . . .' He heard a *clink* after about a three-second count. He struggled with some mental arithmetic and discovered to his irritation that he had forgotten how to figure it. *Rotting innards and mossy brained. It would be difficult to convince anyone that I was ever a paratrooper or that I'm supposed to be an engineer. I don't know that I could convince myself.*

For Carol's benefit he muttered a guess. 'Hundred feet maybe. There must be a prominent ledge at about that level.'

She gazed solemnly and silently into the blackness of the hole.

He tried other trajectories and finally counted better than four seconds before the first sound, this time a distant splash.

'About two hundred and seventy or eighty feet if you disregard drag,' Carol said, after a moment of silence.

Drag, schmag! Shades of the space age! Yet he could not help feeling an obscure admiration for her, maybe even pride.

'I think we still haven't reached bottom,' David said.

'That's possible,' Carol said gravely.

'Would you like to try?'

'All right.'

She tried several times, but her throwing arm was not as good as her physics.

'Let's let Michael,' she said finally.

He was in the process of turning when he heard the sodden cracking of rotten wood and Mike's sharp cry. The fence post that he had been leaning against had suddenly snapped and Mike was plunging down the steep side of the funnel six feet to one side of where David and Carol were crouched. Instantly David launched his body in a horizontal line of motion, striking dank earth flat-out, skidding across and down, even in this paroxysm of motion, outraged, thinking: *My God, I might have known he'd do that.* His hands clutched at the earth and closed on tenuous sassafras roots. His motion stopped coincident with the impact of Mike's body from above. His own body shifted downward with the impact and in slow, creeping motion moved to within inches of the brink of the 'well'. His face was pressed into the earth and his body felt so poised on the edge of further movement that he wondered if he dared speak.

He tried it. 'Mike?'

'Dad?' He could feel the trembling in Mike's body, hear it in his hushed voice.

'Get hold of something, boy.'

'I'm scared to move.'

'Move real slow. Get hold of a root.'

'I can't. . .'

'*Do* it!'

'Dad.' Carol spoke as if in the imminence of a snake's strike. 'You're mighty close to the hole, Dad.'

'I know, I know. I know that. Get a stick, Carol. A strong one. Long enough. Hurry!'

He heard her quick steps up the side of the funnel, soon after heard the snapping of a branch up above.

At least I can depend on her not to get a rotten one.

He felt the faintest shifting of the earth beneath him. 'Hurry, Carol!' He still did not dare to try to move his head in an attempt to look for her.

'I'm here,' she said after a moment.

'Brace yourself on the log and reach out with the stick so Mike can grab it.'

'All right. . . Here, Mike—*grab!*'

'I . . . can't,' Mike said. 'I'm scared. . . Dad?'

'Do it, Mike. You've got to do it.'

He felt a slight, tentative movement as Mike extended a hand towards the stick.

'All right,' he heard Carol say. 'Now the other hand . . . slowly . . . Got it?'

He felt Mike nod, then felt the boy's weight slowly coming off his body.

'I've got you,' Carol said. 'You dig your feet in as best you can and I'll do the pulling.'

He felt Mike's body complete its departure from his and simultaneously the strained damp earth released from the underlying rock and David went over the chasm's brink in a twisting, arching motion, then falling feet-down and spread-eagle. He hit the first ledge in approximately this attitude but leaning slightly forward so that the impact was distributed fairly evenly along his thighs, belly and chest and the under-surfaces of his arms. He hit clawing and scrabbling for a purchase on the damp stone. He pressed his body to the stone and felt the final momentum of his fall come to a slithering tenuous halt on the rounded contour of the ledge. It was only when his motion stopped that he was aware of the shrill screams from above.

In his delicate balance on the ledge he couldn't bring himself to use his lungs, from which most of the air had been forced by his flat impact against the stone. Then he could not forestall the reflex any longer. In a raucous inhalation he sucked in air and felt a slight downward shift of his body. He dug his fingernails into the stone, bringing the slithering motion to another perilous halt. His feet in this last movement had left the rock and projected out over the chasm below. His hands had found some small cross-running ridges in the stone, but his fingers already had begun to ache, all the strength of his body, it seemed, concentrated at their stiffened tips.

'Daddy! Daddy! Oh, Daddy, Daddy!'

He recognized through his stunned senses the terror-stricken voice of Carol. He steeled himself for an answering call. He didn't know whether or not he could talk at all or, if he did, whether he could do it without destroying his pitiful purchase on the ledge.

'Daddy!' Now he could distinguish both their voices, and with that he had his first real knowledge that Mike had not fallen too. It at least gave his plight some meaning. He imagined them crawling out on the log or venturing upon the treacherous slope of the funnel in an effort to see him.

'Carol,' he said in a hoarse whisper. His fingers remained clamped to the stone. 'Mike? Can you hear me?'

'Yes, Daddy. Yes.' They, too, were whispering, as if they were as aware as he was of his delicate balance on the ledge.

'Carol, don't endanger yourselves. I'm all right. But . . . listen, honey. Mike, I'm going to need help. Fast as you can.'

I don't know, I don't. . . I couldn't possibly hang on long enough.

'Mike?'

'Yes, Daddy?'

'Mike, do you think you could find your way home?'

'Yessir! I'll . . . find it.'

'Listen carefully, boy. Tell mother to call the spelunkers.'

'Cave explorers,' he heard Carol say.

'Yes. Tell them your daddy . . . tell them I'm in a deep hole— Bottomless Well. They know about it. Need rope, climbing equipment.'

'Yessir.' His voice sounded steady enough under the circumstances.

'Daddy,' Carol said, 'I can see you. Can you hang on?'

'I don't . . . I don't know. . . Mike, you hurry. Follow the path . . . Carol, you stay here with me?'

'Yes, Daddy, I won't leave.'

'Go now, Mike. . .'

'Yessir!' His voice was already receding.

'Carol?'

'Yes, Daddy?'

'Is Mike gone? . . . Tell him to take care, and tell him . . . tell him . . . that I love him.'

'All right, Dad—' Her voice broke off abruptly.

My God, have they heard it from me so seldom?

He thought he felt a slight creeping of his body on the stone and made a special effort to check his handhold, looking carefully at each of his fingers in turn. His hands looked spatulate and froglike on the rock, the tendons showing through flesh like taut cables. Oddly he was not afraid, at least at that moment he wasn't. He felt a profound animal alertness the like of which he couldn't remember having felt since his combat days. He also felt the beginning of a kind of tender sadness that he would have found impossible to define.

In the waiting silence he took time to try to assay his position —and his chances of survival. *At least as a paratrooper,* he thought wryly, *I've had some training and experience in the business of falling. It's not as new to me as a lot of other things are.* He calculated from the feel of the fall and from an educated guess as to which of the pre-observed shelves of rock he had hit, that he had fallen twenty or thirty feet. He was most certainly bruised and abraded, but as far as he could tell, unbroken—except maybe for a cracked rib or two. With a keened inner ear he tried to plumb the sounds and feelings of his insides, but he could not penetrate the numbness.

He turned his thoughts to the almost inevitable *next* fall. Movement upward to a safer and less demanding perch was unthinkable: his first effort would certainly send him plunging again. And yet he was certain too that he could not hang on for the hour or maybe two that it would take for help to come . . . That is, if it came at all. It was his sad admission that he did not know how much trust he could place in Mike because he had not, as far as he could recall, ever before tested his trustworthiness.

He was suddenly aware of motion on the rock. Focusing his eyes, he saw that it was a small spotted salamander waddling by not three inches from the end of his nose. Fascinated, he watched its progress across the ledge. To the salamander this stone, in this hole in the ground, was a native dwelling, a place where all the vital functions of life were carried out. Here in its home he, David Masters, homo sapiens of sorts, waged a ludicrous war of survival—an injured, out-of-place animal, clumsy, clinging with desperation to the alien rock.

I wonder how the salamander would do in my *world? No worse than I have—ill-adapted, sick at heart—desperately clinging to unsubstantial things like self-pity, infidelity . . . alcoholism. Yes, I'm that too; I would have called it any word but that, but that's what I am.*

He felt the slightest giving of his body on the stone— a concession to gravity, a low coefficient of friction and fatigue.

He tightened his fingers.

It would be nice to know what's directly below, he thought. *I don't remember, or the light didn't shine down that far.*

He thought of the flashlight in his hip pocket. *Go ahead, Dave boy, pull it out and shine it down there where you're gonna be. Enlighten yourself. Go ahead.*

He clutched the stone, letting the first wave of hysteria wash over him and then, recognizing it, putting it aside for the moment.

Perhaps a lucky fall and a kinder ledge down there? . . . Or death. He let himself think about that rationally. Why not? He'd already accepted it. He'd been killing himself for years. The stone could be no less kind in its infliction of death. In fact, it undoubtedly would be more merciful—certainly without rancour . . .

Let go, you idiot! You'll never have a better chance.

'Daddy?'

He curved his aching fingers into the unyielding stone.

'Yes, Carol?'

'I've got a grape vine. I'm going to let it down and swing it over to you.'

'Honey, honey. . . Carol . . .'

'It's very strong, Daddy. I had to chop it off at the bottom with a sharp rock.'

'Carol . . .'

'Daddy, I'm letting it down. You'll feel it touch your back in a minute.'

Tears flowed from his eyes and salted the stone under his cheek. He tried to look up but couldn't complete the effort. He felt something brush his right shoulder like a warm caress.

'Carol—' He choked on the word. 'Honey, how have you got it tied?'

'I tried to tie it around the log, Daddy, but it's too thick; I can't bend it enough.'

'Carol, honey, don't bother, don't—'

'Daddy, I've got my legs wrapped around the log. I can hold it, I can.'

'No, Carol darling. I'd just pull *you* in. Besides, you couldn't possibly pull me up.'

'I could hold you till they come.'

He tried to stifle his free-flowing tears. *If only I could give my life meaningfully for her,* he thought with hopeless regret.

'No, Carol, I don't think I could let go to reach for it, anyhow. Now you pull it back up, honey.'

It seemed he could *feel* the vine receding from him and it made him feel infinitely lonely.

'Carol?'

'Yes?' He could hear the helpless defeat in her voice.

'Thank you, darling... I love you.' It was getting easier to say.

Unexpectedly, as if he had been struck a sudden blow from above, his grip failed. He slid off the ledge and fell, essentially in the spread-eagle attitude of his earlier fall. He had no time to resign himself to anything before his extended legs smashed again into merciless stone. He hit differently this time, less flat, taking a large part of the impact on one leg; sharp pain in that leg informed him too that he had hit with more damage to himself than before. But again, before sliding over the new precipice, he flattened himself to the rock and brought his motion to a stop. His purchase was somewhat better, more secure, than before, but his strength had been greatly sapped by his previous effort.

'Daddeeeeee!' He heard the wail from above, profoundly regretting the ordeal of terror he was inflicting on her. He laboriously sucked air into his lungs.

'Carol. I'm . . . all right, honey. I'm on another ledge. I . . . might be able to hang on.'

'Daddy, I can't see you any more!'

I know. Much darker. . .

So this is the way it ends. Maybe befitting enough; swallowed up by the boyhood mountain that he loved. . . Determined he had been to return to gentle Garth and its magnificent mountain—Buena Vista—and on an expansive wooded lot build a fine house with his own two hands and his native intelligence—a house with a fieldstone fireplace big enough to warm a man's soul, and massive oak beams, like security itself, overhead. Then live an active, creative, meaningful life, full of good cheer, with Grace—and with the most wondrous children of their flesh. . .

And they lived happily never after.

'Daddy?'

He had to think a moment, then gather himself.

'DADDY!'

'Yes, yes, Carol. I'm here.'

'Oh.' A silence. 'Daddy, will you say something every now and then so I'll know you're all right?'

'Yes, honey. I'm sorry. Every minute I'll tell you I love you. Okay?'

'Oh, Daddy, Daddy. I feel so *bad.*'

He thought he felt something splash down upon him and momentarily clung to the belief that it was her tears. It was as if she had touched him and he felt less lonely.

He let a delirium wash over him.

Ah, such golden dreams! . . . But he pooped out, got diverted and perverted—overly involved with failure and preoccupied with advancing years; blighted with cynicism, infidelity, mistrust and nuclearitis (*At least I built, I mean* completed, *the fall-out shelter. I finished it, no doubt, because it sickened me. It's typical of my recent attitude and behaviour*). . .

'I love you, Carol,' he called up to her.

'I love you, Daddy,' she called back.

If we love each other why haven't we shown it? What have we been doing all this time? . . .

A far cry, David, from the Golden Man with his Golden Dream. Where did the degenerative process start? . . . Who knows? . . . It seemed that cause and effect were lost in a hopeless tangle of negativeness. Golden Man, after two wars and much searching, returns to Garth with his Golden Wife to work at the thing he had once been trained to do: engineering. Maybe that was it; maybe there had been too many years and too many other things between the learning and the doing.

Maybe some obscure incident he couldn't even remember had conveyed that to him and started a chain reaction of doubt. At any rate, he had failed to secure the feeling of competence and of being respected in his profession. And the lack of those things, which had been a basic part of his plan and a basic part of his need, could have started a pattern of defeat in him that he could never overcome. . .

And Garth. What had happened to his beloved Garth? No longer quiet, no longer a sleepy Southern town, no longer the embodiment of a boyhood memory. It was not even *called* Garth any more but names like 'Space City' and 'Rocketville, U.S.A.' Not a town at all any more, but a mad-house of bustle and outrageous growth and profit and spoilage.

At least that's the way he had looked at it, even if it and its missile business, its dynamic Flint Arsenal, *had* provided him with the means to return. . .

Man-o-man! . . . I could use a drink. As he pressed his life-worn flesh to the deathless stone, he thought in another flash of hysteria: *wouldn't it be something if I, needing a drink now maybe for the first time in my life, really* needing *it, had the flask, miraculously unbroken, in my hip pocket . . . and not being able to get to it. Needing it just like I need that flashlight and both of them a million miles away on my butt.* A perverse laughter bubbled in him.

The next fall caught him almost unaware of its occurrence. In mid-air, as he sank again into the abyss, realization struck him and instinctively he made an effort to control the attitude of his body. He hit jarringly on his legs and his right hip and sank wearily into a broken heap on the new ledge. His senses were dulled almost beyond physical pain and in one sense he was filled with a fatal hopelessness; yet as he felt himself slipping once again over an inevitable brink he clutched the impersonally, sadistic rock and, momentarily at least, found a purchase.

Through his shocked senses he listened for sounds from above. *Thank God. I don't believe she even knew about that one.*

'Carol?' His voice floated up through the tube of stone.

'Yes, Daddy.' Her voice sounded small and weary—weary beyond her age.

'Carol . . . it is perfectly natural for a girl of any age to . . . to want a horse.'

'Daddy . . . don't—'

'You're a good girl, a good person, Carol. You ask for little. You'll have your horse. . . Tell Mother—'

His senses blackened and with infinite sadness and regret he slid off into his waiting void, even in his delirious exhaustion clutching for some useful and substantial handhold; and then, not finding it, falling, trying to orient his plunging body into some rightful order of descent. . .

He opened his eyes to a spot of light directly above; bending into the light was a hallucination, then another.

Sudden memory signalled a sharp warning to his brain, spurted adrenalin into his veins. His arms moved like pistons, hands clutching at stone. They found no substance and he knew he was falling again. His body twisted in an effort to gain the proper attitude of falling; sharp pains shot through his legs.

'He's conscious, Ben. Help me hold him.'

Reality returned to his brain and, more slowly, to the desperate reflexes of his body.

Conscious? Conscious of what? . . . Oh, yes . . .

He felt firm hands restraining his arms.

'It's all right, fella. Just take it easy.'

In one arm he felt the distant prick of a needle. He looked up at the owner of the voice, a bespectacled face loosely attached to a small wiry body. He slowly let out his taut breath. 'So . . . I finally stopped falling.' His voice sounded hollow and hardly recognizable as his own.

'You did. It's a fairly broad shelf. Covered with several inches of silt, luckily for you.'

Another face leaned out of the shadows. 'My hat's off to you, mister. It's bad enough coming down here on a rope. You must be living right.'

In a distant corner of his mind David heard the ring of ironic laughter.

The bespectacled man, apparently a doctor, listened to his chest with a stethoscope.

He nodded. 'We'll hoist you up now.'

'My family? Grace?'

'They're up there.'

His memory leapt. '*Mike?*'

The doctor chuckled. 'You mean the new sprint champion of

Tuscahatchee County? I don't believe a Sherman tank could remove him.'

David and the doctor gazed at each other.

'You're pretty busted up, but as far as I can tell there's nothing we can't patch.'

David looked up at the rough circle of daylight above him. He felt an old identity flowing into him like the return of a benevolent ghost.

'Doctor,' he said, smiling with a new inner bearing that was at once profound and risible, 'what's it like on the outside?'

The man smiled back at him. 'You'll soon be finding out.'

'Doctor,' David said, 'you can say that again.'

To Build a Fire *by Jack London*

Day had broken cold and grey, exceedingly cold and grey, when the man turned aside from the main Yukon trail and climbed the high earth-bank, where a dim and little-travelled trail led eastward through the fat spruce timberland. It was a steep bank, and he paused for breath at the top, excusing the act to himself by looking at his watch. It was nine o'clock. There was no sun nor hint of sun, though there was not a cloud in the sky. It was a clear day, and yet there seemed an intangible pall over the face of things, a subtle gloom that made the day dark, and that was due to the absence of sun. This fact did not worry the man. He was used to the lack of sun. It had been days since he had seen the sun, and he knew that a few more days must pass before that cheerful orb, due south, would just peep above the skyline and dip immediately from view.

The man flung a look back along the way he had come. The Yukon lay a mile wide and hidden under three feet of ice. On top of this ice were as many feet of snow. It was all pure white, rolling in gentle undulations where the ice-jams of the freeze-up had formed. North and south, as far as the eye could see, it was unbroken white, save for a dark hair-line that curved and twisted from around the spruce-covered island to the south, and that curved and twisted away into the north, where it disappeared behind another spruce-covered island. This dark hair-line was the trail—the main trail—that led south five hundred miles to the Chilcoot Pass, Dyea, and salt water; and that led north seventy miles to Dawson, and still on to the north a thousand miles to Nulato, and finally to St Michael on Bering Sea, a thousand miles and a half a thousand more.

But all this—the mysterious, far-reaching hair-line trail, the absence of sun from the sky, the tremendous cold, and the strangeness and weirdness of it all—made no impression on the man. It was not because he was long used to it. He was a newcomer in the land, a *chechaquo*, and this was his first winter. The trouble with him was that he was without imagination. He was quick and alert in the things of life, but only in the things, and not in the significances. Fifty degrees below zero meant eighty-odd degrees of frost. Such fact impressed him as being cold and uncomfortable, and that was all. It did not lead him to meditate upon his frailty as a creature of temperature, and upon man's frailty in general, able only to live within certain narrow limits of heat and cold; and from there on it did not lead him to the conjectural field of immortality and man's place in the universe. Fifty degrees below zero stood for a bite of frost that hurt and that must be guarded against by the use of mittens, ear-flaps, warm moccasins, and thick socks. Fifty degrees below zero was to him just precisely fifty degrees below zero. That there should be anything more to it than that was a thought that never entered his head.

As he turned to go on, he spat speculatively. There was a sharp, explosive crackle that startled him. He spat again. And again, in the air, before it could fall to the snow, the spittle crackled. He knew that at fifty below spittle crackled on the snow, but this spittle had crackled in the air. Undoubtedly it was colder than fifty below—how much colder he did not know. But the temperature did not matter. He was bound for the old claim on the left fork of Henderson Creek, where the boys were already. They had come over across the divide from the Indian Creek country, while he had come the roundabout way to take a look at the possibilities of getting out logs in the spring from the islands in the Yukon. He would be in camp by six o'clock; a bit after dark, it was true, but the boys would be there, a fire would be going, and a hot supper would be ready. As for lunch, he pressed his hand against the protruding bundle under his jacket. It was also under his shirt, wrapped up in a handkerchief, and lying against the naked skin. It was the only way to keep the biscuits from freezing. He smiled agreeably to himself as he thought of those biscuits, each cut open and sopped in bacon grease, and each enclosing a generous slice of fried bacon.

He plunged in among the big spruce trees. The trail was faint. A foot of snow had fallen since the last sled had passed over, and he was glad he was without a sled, travelling light. In fact, he carried nothing but the lunch wrapped in the handkerchief. He was surprised, however, at the cold. It certainly was cold, he concluded, as he rubbed his numbed nose and cheekbones with his mittened hand. He was a warm-whiskered man, but the hair on his face did not protect the high cheekbones and the eager nose that thrust itself aggressively into the frosty air.

At the man's heels trotted a dog, a big native husky, the proper wolf-dog, grey-coated and without any visible or temperamental difference from its brother, the wild wolf. The animal was depressed by the tremendous cold. It knew that it was no time for travelling. Its instinct told it a truer tale than was told to the man by the man's judgement. In reality, it was not merely colder than fifty below zero; it was colder than sixty below, than seventy below. It was seventy-five below zero. Since the freezing-point is thirty-two above zero it meant that one hundred and seven degrees of frost obtained. The dog did not know anything about thermometers. Possibly in its brain there was no sharp consciousness of a condition of very cold such as was in the man's brain. But the brute had its instinct. It experienced a vague but menacing apprehension that subdued it and made it slink along at the man's heels, and that made it question eagerly every unwonted movement of the man as if expecting him to go into camp or to seek shelter somewhere and build a fire. The dog had learned fire, and it wanted fire, or else to burrow under the snow and cuddle its warmth away from the air.

The frozen moisture of its breathing had settled on its fur in a fine powder of frost, and especially were its jowls, muzzle, and eyelashes whitened by its crystalled breath. The man's red beard and moustache were likewise frosted, but more solidly, the deposit taking the form of ice and increasing with every warm, moist breath he exhaled. Also, the man was chewing tobacco, and the muzzle of ice held his lips so rigidly that he was unable to clear his chin when he expelled the juice. The result was that a crystal beard of the colour and solidity of amber was increasing its length on his chin. If he fell down it would shatter itself, like glass, into brittle fragments. But he did not mind the appendage. It was the penalty all tobacco-chewers paid in that country, and he had been out before in two cold snaps. They had not been so cold as this, he knew, but by the spirit thermometer at Sixty Mile he knew they had been registered at fifty below and at fifty-five.

He held on through the level stretch of woods for several miles, crossed a wide flat of niggerheads, and dropped down a bank to the frozen bed of a small stream. This was Henderson Creek, and he knew he was ten miles from the forks. He looked at his watch. It was ten o'clock. He was making four miles an hour, and he calculated that he would arrive at the forks at half-past twelve. He decided to celebrate that event by eating his lunch there.

The dog dropped in again at his heels, with a tail drooping discouragement as the man swung along the creek-bed. The furrow of the old sled-trail was plainly visible, but a dozen inches of snow covered the marks of the last runners. In a month no man had come up or down that silent creek. The man held steadily on. He was not much given to thinking, and just then particularly he had nothing to think about save that he would eat lunch at the forks and that at six o'clock he would be in camp with the boys. There was nobody to talk to; and, had there been, speech would have been impossible because of the ice-muzzle on his mouth. So he continued monotonously to chew tobacco and to increase the length of his amber beard.

Once in a while the thought reiterated itself that it was very cold and that he had never experienced such cold. As he walked along he rubbed his cheek-bones and nose with the back of his mittened hand. He did this automatically, now and again changing hands. But rub as he would, the instant he stopped his cheek-bones went numb, and the following instant the end of his nose went numb. He was sure to frost his cheeks; he knew that, and experienced a pang of regret that he had not devised a nose-strap of the sort Bud wore in cold snaps. Such a strap passed across the cheeks as well, and saved them. But it didn't matter much, after all. What were frosted cheeks? A bit painful, that was all; they were never serious.

Empty as the man's mind was of thoughts, he was keenly observant, and he noticed the changes in the creek, the curves and bends and timberjams, and always he sharply noted where he placed his feet. Once, coming around a bend, he shied abruptly like a startled horse, curved away from the place where he had been walking, and retreated several paces back along the trail. The creek he knew was frozen clear to the bottom—no creek could contain water in that arctic winter—

but he knew also that there were springs that bubbled out from the hillsides and ran along under the snow and on top of the ice of the creek. He knew that the coldest snaps never froze these springs, and he knew likewise their danger. They were traps. They hid pools of water under the snow that might be three inches deep, or three feet. Sometimes a skin of ice half an inch thick covered them, and in turn was covered by the snow. Sometimes there were alternate layers of water and ice-skin, so that when one broke through he kept on breaking through for a while, sometimes wetting himself to the waist.

That was why he had shied in such panic. He had felt the give under his feet and heard the crackle of a snow-hidden ice-skin. And to get his feet wet in such a temperature meant trouble and danger. At the very least it meant delay, for he would be forced to stop and build a fire, and under its protection to bare his feet while he dried his socks and moccasins. He stood and studied the creek-bed and its banks, and decided that the flow of water came from the right. He reflected awhile, rubbing his nose and cheeks and skirted to the left, stepping gingerly and testing the footing for each step. Once clear of the danger, he took a fresh chew of tobacco and swung along at his four-mile gait.

In the course of the next two hours he came upon several similar traps. Usually the snow above the hidden pools had a sunken, candied appearance that advertised the danger. Once again, however, he had a close call; and once, suspecting danger, he compelled the dog to go on in front. The dog did not want to go. It hung back until the man shoved it forward, and then it went quickly across the white, unbroken surface. Suddenly it broke through, floundered to one side, and got away to firmer footing. It had wet its forefeet and legs and almost immediately the water that clung to it turned to ice. It made quick efforts to lick the ice off its legs, then dropped down in the snow and began to bite out the ice that had formed between the toes. This was a matter of instinct. To permit the ice to remain would mean sore feet. It did not know this. It merely obeyed the mysterious prompting that arose from the deep crypts of its being. But the man knew, having achieved a judgement on the subject, and he removed the mitten from his right hand and helped tear out the ice-particles. He did not expose his fingers more than a minute and was astonished at the swift numbness that smote them. It certainly was cold. He pulled on the mitten hastily, and beat the hand savagely across his chest.

At twelve o'clock the day was at its brightest. Yet the sun was too far south on its winter journey to clear the horizon. The bulge of the earth intervened between it and Henderson Creek, where the man walked under a clear sky at noon and cast no shadow. At half-past twelve, to the minute, he arrived at the forks of the creek. He was pleased at the speed he had made. If he kept it up, he would certainly be with the boys by six. He unbuttoned his jacket and shirt and drew forth his lunch. The action consumed no more than a quarter of a minute, yet in that brief moment the numbness laid hold of the exposed fingers. He did not put the mitten on, but instead, struck the fingers a dozen sharp smashes against his leg. Then he sat down on a snow-covered log to eat. The sting that followed upon the striking of his fingers against his leg ceased so quickly that he was startled. He had had no chance to take a bite of biscuit. He struck the fingers repeatedly and returned them to the mitten, baring the other hand for the purpose of eating. He tried to take a mouthful but the ice-muzzle prevented. He had forgotten to build a fire and thaw out. He chuckled at his foolishness, and as he chuckled he noted the numbness creeping into the exposed fingers. Also, he noted that the stinging which had first come to his toes when he sat down was already passing away. He wondered whether the toes were warm or numbed. He moved them inside the moccasins and decided that they were numbed.

He pulled the mitten on hurriedly and stood up. He was a bit frightened. He stamped up and down until the stinging returned into the feet. It certainly was cold was his thought. That man from Sulphur Creek had spoken the truth when telling how cold it sometimes got in the country. And he had laughed at him at the time! That showed one must not be too sure of things. There was no mistake about it, it *was* cold. He strode up and down, stamping his feet and threshing his arms, until reassured by the returning warmth. Then he got out matches and proceeded to make a fire. From the undergrowth, where high water of the previous spring had lodged a supply of seasoned twigs, he got his firewood. Working carefully from a small beginning, he soon had a roaring fire, over which he thawed the ice from his face and in the protection of which he ate his biscuits. For the moment the cold of space was outwitted. The dog took satisfaction in the fire, stretching out close enough for warmth and far enough away to escape being singed.

When the man had finished, he filled his pipe and took his comfortable time over a smoke. Then he pulled on his mittens, settled the ear-flaps of his cap firmly about his ears, and took the creek trail up the left fork. The dog was disappointed and yearned back towards the fire. This man did not know cold. Possibly all the generations of his ancestry had been ignorant of cold, of real cold, of cold one hundred and seven degrees below freezing-point. But the dog knew; all its ancestry knew, and it had inherited the knowledge. And it knew that it was not good to walk abroad in such fearful cold. It was the time to lie snug in a hole in the snow and wait for a curtain of cloud to be drawn across the face of outer space whence this cold came. On the other hand, there was no keen intimacy between the dog and the man. The one was the toil-slave of the other, and the only caresses it had ever received were the caresses of the whip-lash and of harsh and menacing throat-sounds that threatened the whip-lash. So the dog made no effort to communicate its apprehension to the man. It was not concerned in the welfare of the man; it was for its own sake that it yearned back towards the fire. But the man whistled and spoke to it with the sound of whip-lashes, and the dog swung in at the man's heels and followed after.

The man took a chew of tobacco and proceeded to start a new amber beard. Also, his moist breath quickly powdered with white his moustache, eyebrows and lashes. There did not seem to be so many springs on the left fork of the Henderson, and for half an hour the man saw no signs of any. And then it happened. At the place where there were no signs, where the soft, unbroken snow seemed to advertise solidity beneath, the man broke through. It was not deep. He wet himself halfway to the knees before he floundered out to the firm crust.

He was angry, and cursed his luck aloud. He had hoped to get into camp with the boys at six o'clock, and this would delay him an hour, for he would have to build a fire and dry out his footgear. This was imperative at that low temperature—he knew that much; and he turned aside to the bank, which he climbed. On top, tangled in the underbrush about the trunks of several small spruce trees, was a high-water deposit of dry firewood—sticks and twigs, principally, but also larger portions of seasoned branches and fine, dry, last-year's grasses. He threw down several large pieces on top of the snow. This served for a foundation and prevented the young flame from drowning itself in the snow it otherwise would melt. The flame he got by touching a match to a small shred of birch-bark that he took from his pocket. This burned even more readily than paper. Placing it on the foundation, he fed the young flames with wisps of dry grass and with the tiniest dry twigs.

He worked slowly and carefully, keenly aware of his danger. Gradually, as the flame grew stronger, he increased the size of the twigs with which he fed it. He squatted in the snow, pulling the twigs out from their entanglement in the brush and feeding directly to the flame. He knew there must be no failure. When it is seventy-five below zero, a man must not fail in his first attempt to build a fire—that is, if his feet are wet. If his feet are dry, and he fails, he can run along the trail for half a mile and restore his circulation. But the circulation of wet and freezing feet cannot be restored by running when it is seventy-five below. No matter how fast he runs, the wet feet will freeze the harder.

All this the man knew. The old-timer on Sulphur Creek had told him about it the previous fall, and now he was appreciating the advice. Already all sensation had gone out of his feet. To build the fire he had been forced to remove his mittens, and the fingers had quickly gone numb. His pace of four miles an hour had kept his heart pumping blood to the surface of his body and to all the extremities. But the instant he stopped, the action of the pump eased down. The cold of space smote the unprotected tip of the planet, and he, being on that unprotected tip, received the full force of the blow. The blood of his body recoiled before it. The blood was alive, like the dog, and like the dog it wanted to hide away and cover itself up from the fearful cold. So long as he walked four miles an hour, he pumped that blood, willy-nilly, to the surface; but now it ebbed away and sank down into the recesses of his body. The extremities were the first to feel its absence. His wet feet froze the faster, and his exposed fingers numbed the faster, though they had not yet begun to freeze. Nose and cheeks were already freezing, while the skin of all his body chilled as it lost its blood.

But he was safe. Toes and nose and cheeks would be only touched by the frost, for the fire was beginning to burn with strength. He was feeding it with twigs the size of his finger. In another minute he would be able to feed it with branches the size of his wrist and then he could remove his wet footgear, and while it dried he could keep his naked feet warm by the fire, rubbing them at first, of course, with snow. The fire was a success. He was safe. He remembered the advice of the old-timer on Sulphur Creek and smiled. The old-timer had been very serious in laying down the law that no man must travel alone in the Klondike after fifty below. Well, here he was; he had had an accident; he was alone; and he saved himself. Those old-timers were rather womanish, some of them, he thought. All a man had to do was to keep his head and he was all right. Any man who was a man could travel alone. But it was surprising, the rapidity with which his cheeks and nose were freezing. And he had not thought his fingers could go lifeless in so short a time. Lifeless they were, for he could scarcely make them move together to grip a twig, and they seemed remote from his body and from him. When he touched a twig, he had to look and see whether or not he had hold of it. The wires were pretty well down between him and his finger-ends.

All of which counted for little. There was the fire, snapping and crackling and promising life with every dancing flame. He started to untie his moccasins. They were coated with ice; the thick German socks were like sheaths of iron halfway to the knees; and the moccasin strings were like rods of steel all twisted and knotted as by some conflagration. For a moment he tugged with his numbed fingers, then, realizing the folly of it, he drew his sheath-knife.

But before he could cut the strings, it happened. It was his own fault or, rather, his mistake. He should not have built the fire under the spruce tree. He should have built it in the open. But it had been easier to pull the twigs from the brush and drop them directly on the fire. Now the tree under which he had done this carried a weight of snow on its boughs. No wind had blown for weeks, and each bough was fully freighted. Each time he had pulled a twig he had communicated a slight agitation to the tree—an imperceptible agitation so far as he was concerned, but an agitation sufficient to bring about the disaster. High up in the tree one bough capsized its load of snow. This fell on the boughs beneath, capsizing them. This process continued, spreading out and involving the whole tree. It grew like an avalanche, and it descended without warning upon the man and the fire, and the fire was blotted out! Where it had burned was a mantle of fresh and disordered snow.

The man was shocked. It was as though he had just heard his own sentence of death. For a moment he sat and stared at the spot where the fire had been. Then he grew very calm. Perhaps the old-timer on Sulphur Creek was right. If he had only had a trail-mate he would have been in no danger now. The trail-mate could have built the fire. Well, it was up to him to build the fire over again, and this second time there must be no failure. Even if he succeeded, he would most likely lose some toes. His feet must be badly frozen by now, and there would be some time before the second fire was ready.

Such were his thoughts, but he did not sit and think them. He was busy all the time they were passing through his mind. He made a new foundation for a fire, this time in the open where no treacherous tree could blot it out. Next, he gathered dry grasses and tiny twigs from the high-water flotsam. He could not bring his fingers together to pull them out, but he was able to gather them by the handful. In this way he got many rotten twigs and bits of green moss that were undesirable, but it was the best he could do. He worked methodically, even collecting an armful of the larger branches to be used later when the fire gathered strength. And all the while the dog sat and watched him, a certain yearning wistfulness in its eyes, for it looked upon him as the fire-provider, and the fire was slow in coming.

When all was ready, the man reached in his pocket for a second piece of birch-bark. He knew the bark was there, and, though he could not feel it with his fingers, he could hear its crisp rustling as he fumbled for it. Try as he would, he could not clutch hold of it. And all the time, in his consciousness, was the knowledge that each instant his feet were freezing. This thought tended to put him in a panic, but he fought against it and kept calm. He pulled on his mittens with his teeth, and threshed his arms back and forth, beating his hands with all his might against his sides. He did this sitting down, and he stood up to do it; and all the while the dog sat in the snow, its wolf-brush of a tail curled around warmly over its forefeet, its sharp wolf-ears pricked forward intently as it watched the man. And the man as he beat and threshed with his arms and hands, felt a great surge of envy as he regarded the creature that was warm and secure in its natural covering.

After a time he was aware of the first far-away signals of sensation in his beaten fingers. The faint tingling grew stronger till it evolved into a stinging ache that was excruciating, but which the man hailed with satisfaction. He stripped the mitten from his right hand and fetched forth the birch-bark. The exposed fingers were quickly going numb again. Next he brought out his bunch of sulphur matches. But the tremendous cold had already driven the life out of his fingers. In his effort to separate one match from the others, the whole bunch fell in the snow. He tried to pick it out of the snow but failed. The dead fingers could neither touch nor clutch. He was very careful. He drove the thought of his freezing feet, and nose, and cheeks out of his mind, devoting his whole soul to the matches. He watched, using the sense of vision in place of that of touch, and when he saw his fingers on each side the bunch, he closed— that is, he willed to close them, for the wires were down, and the fingers did not obey. He pulled the mitten on the right hand and beat it fiercely against his knee. Then, with both mittened hands, he scooped the bunch of matches, along with much snow, into his lap. Yet he was no better off.

After much manipulation he managed to get the bunch between the heels of his mittened hands. In this fashion he carried it to his mouth. The ice crackled and snapped when by a violent effort he opened his mouth. He drew the lower jaw in, curled the upper lip out of the way, and scraped the bunch with his upper teeth in order to separate a match. He succeeded in getting one which he dropped on his lap. He was no better off. He could not pick it up. Then he devised a way. He picked it up in his teeth and scratched it on his leg. Twenty times he scratched before he succeeded in lighting it. As it flamed he held it with his teeth to the birch-bark. But the burning brimstone went up his nostrils and into his lungs, causing him to cough spasmodically. The match fell into the snow and went out.

The old-timer on Sulphur Creek was right, he thought in the moment of controlled despair that ensued: after fifty below, a man should travel with a partner. He beat his hands, but failed in exciting any sensation. Suddenly he bared both hands, removing the mittens with his teeth. He caught the whole bunch between the heels of his hands. His arm-muscles not being frozen enabled him to press the hand-heels tightly against the matches. Then he scratched the bunch along his leg. It flared into flame, seventy sulphur matches at once! There was no wind to blow them out. He kept his head to one side to escape the strangling fumes, and held the blazing bunch to the birch-bark. As he so held it, he became aware of sensation in his hand. His flesh was burning. He could smell it. Deep down below the surface he could feel it. The sensation developed into pain that grew acute. And still he endured it, holding the flame of the matches clumsily because his own burning hands were in the way, absorbing most of the flame.

At last, when he could endure no more, he jerked his hands apart. The blazing matches fell sizzling into the snow, but the birch-bark was alight. He began laying dry grasses and the tiniest twigs on the flame. He could not pick and choose, for he had to lift the fuel between the heels of his hands. Small pieces of rotten wood and green moss clung to the twigs, and he bit them off as well as he could with his teeth. He cherished the flame carefully and awkwardly. It meant life, and it must not perish. The withdrawal of blood from the surface of his body now made him begin to shiver, and he grew more awkward. A large piece of moss fell squarely on the little fire. He tried to poke it out with his fingers, but his shivering frame made him poke too far, and he disrupted the nucleus of the little fire, the burning grasses and tiny twigs separating and scattering. He tried to poke them together again, but in spite of the tenseness of the effort, his shivering got away with him and the twigs were hopelessly scattered. Each twig gushed a puff of smoke and went out. The fire-provider had failed. As he looked apathetically about him, his eyes chanced on the dog, sitting across the ruins of the fire from him, in the snow, making restless, hunching movements, slightly lifting one forefoot and then the other, shifting its weight back and forth on them with wistful eagerness.

The sight of the dog put a wild idea into his head. He remembered the tale of the man caught in a blizzard who killed a steer and crawled inside the carcass, and so was saved. He would kill the dog and bury his hands in the warm body until the numbness went out of them. Then he could build another fire. He spoke to the dog, calling it to him; but in his voice was a strange note of fear that frightened the animal, who had never known the man to speak in such a way before. Something was the matter, and its suspicious nature sensed danger—it knew not what danger, but somewhere, somehow, in its brain arose an apprehension of the man. It flattened its ears down at the sound of the man's voice, and its restless, hunching movements and the liftings and shifting of its forefeet became more pronounced; but it would not come to the man. He got on his hands and knees and crawled towards the dog. This unusual posture again excited suspicion, and the animal sidled mincingly away.

The man sat up in the snow for a moment and struggled for calmness. Then he pulled on his mittens by means of his teeth, and got upon his feet. He glanced down at first in order to assure himself that he was really standing up, for the absence of sensation in his feet left him unrelated to the earth. His erect position in itself started to drive the webs of suspicion from the dog's mind; and when he spoke peremptorily, with the sound of whip-lashes in his voice, the dog rendered its customary allegiance and came to him. As it came within reaching distance, the man lost his control. His arms flashed out to the dog and he experienced genuine surprise when he discovered that his hands could not clutch, that there was neither bend nor feeling in the fingers. He had forgotten for the moment that they were frozen and that they were freezing more and more. All this happened quickly, and before the animal could get away, he encircled its body with his arms. He sat down in the snow, and in this fashion held the dog, while it snarled and whined and struggled.

But it was all he could do: hold its body encircled in his arms and sit there. He realized that he could not kill the dog. There was no way to do it. With his helpless hands he could neither draw nor hold his sheath knife nor throttle the animal. He released it, and it plunged wildly away with tail between its legs, and still snarling. It halted forty feet away and surveyed him curiously, with ears sharply pricked forward. The man looked down at his hands in order to locate them and found them hanging on the ends of his arms. It struck him as curious that he should have to use his eyes in order to find out where his hands were. He began threshing his arms back and forth, beating the mittened hands against his sides. He did this for five minutes, violently, and his heart pumped enough blood up to the surface to put a stop to his shivering. But no sensation was aroused in the hands. He had an impression that they hung like weights on the ends of his arms, but when he tried to run the impression down he could not find it.

A certain fear of death, dull and oppressive, came to him. This fear quickly became poignant as he realized that it was no longer a mere matter of freezing his fingers and toes, or of his losing hands and feet, but that it was a matter of life and death with the chances against him. This threw him into a panic, and he turned and ran up the creek-bed along the old, dim trail. The dog joined in behind and kept up with him. He ran blindly, without intention, in fear such as he had never known in his life. Slowly, as he ploughed and floundered through the snow, he began to see things again,—the banks of the creek, the old timber-jams, the leafless aspens, and the sky. The running made him feel better. He did not shiver. Maybe, if he ran on, his feet would thaw out; and, anyway, if he ran far enough, he would reach camp and the boys. Without doubt he would lose some fingers and toes and some of his face; but the boys would take care of him and save the rest of him when he got there. And at the same time there was another thought in his mind that said he would never get to the camp and the boys; that it was too many miles away, that the freezing had too great a start on him, and that he would soon be stiff and dead. This thought he kept in the background and refused to consider. Sometimes it pushed itself forward and demanded to be heard, but he thrust it back and strove to think of other things.

It struck him as curious that he could run at all on feet so frozen that he could not feel them when they struck the earth and took the weight of his body. He seemed to himself to skim along above the surface and to have no connection with the earth. Somewhere he had once seen a winged Mercury, and he wondered if Mercury felt as he felt when skimming over the earth.

His theory of running until he reached camp and the boys had one flaw in it: he lacked the endurance. Several times he stumbled, and finally he tottered, crumpled up, and fell. When he tried to rise, he failed. He must sit and rest, he decided, and next time he would merely walk and keep on going. As he sat and regained his breath, he noted that he was feeling quite warm and comfortable. He was not shivering, and it even seemed that a warm glow had come to his chest and trunk. And yet, when he touched his nose or cheeks, there was no sensation. Running would not thaw them out. Nor would it thaw out his hands and feet. Then the thought came to him that the frozen portions of his body must be extending. He tried to keep this thought down, to forget it, to think of something else; he was aware of the panicky feeling that it caused, and he was afraid of the panic. But the thought asserted itself, and persisted, until it produced a vision of his body totally frozen. This was too much, and he made another wild run along the trail. Once he slowed down to a walk, but the thought of the freezing extending itself made him run again.

And all the time the dog ran with him at his heels. When he fell down a second time it curled its tail over its forefeet and sat in front of him, facing him, curiously eager and intent. The warmth and security of the animal angered him, and he cursed it till it flattened down its ears appeasingly. This time the shivering came more quickly upon the man. He was losing in his battle with the frost. It was creeping into his body from all sides. The thought of it drove him on, but he ran no more than a hundred feet when he staggered and pitched headlong. It was his last panic. When he had recovered his breath and control, he sat up and entertained in his mind the conception of meeting death with dignity. However, the conception did not come to him in such terms. His idea of it was that he had been making a fool of himself, running around like a chicken with its head cut off—such was the simile that occurred to him. Well, he was bound to freeze anyway, and he might as well take it decently. With this new-found peace of mind came the first glimmerings of drowsiness. A good idea, he thought, to sleep off to death. It was like taking an anaesthetic. Freezing was not so bad as people thought. There were lots worse ways to die.

He pictured the boys finding his body next day. Suddenly he found himself with them, coming along the trail and looking for himself. And, still with them, he came around a turn in the trail and found himself lying in the snow. He did not belong with himself any more, for even then he was out of himself, standing with the boys and looking at himself in the snow. It certainly was cold, was his thought. When he got back to the States he could tell the folks what real cold was. He drifted on from this to a vision of the old-timer on Sulphur Creek. He could see him quite clearly, warm and comfortable, and smoking a pipe.

'You were right, old hoss; you were right,' the man mumbled to the old-timer of Sulphur Creek.

Then the man drowsed off into what seemed to him the most comfortable and satisfying sleep he had ever known. The dog sat facing him and waiting. The brief day drew to a close in a long, slow twilight. There were no signs of a fire to be made, and, besides, never in the dog's experience had it known a man to sit like that in the snow and make no fire. As the twilight drew on, its eager yearning for the fire mastered it, and with a great lifting and shifting of forefeet, it whined softly, then flattened its ears down in anticipation of being chidden by the man. But the man remained silent. Later, the dog whined loudly. And still later it crept close to the man and caught the scent of death. This made the animal bristle and back away. A little longer it delayed, howling under the stars that leaped and danced and shone brightly in the cold sky. Then it turned and trotted up the trail in the direction of the camp it knew, where were the other food-providers and fire-providers.

Notes

THE MAN WHO WASN'T SCARED

2 *Home Office*: government department responsible among other matters for police and crime

3 *Yard*: Scotland Yard

5 *bedlam*: madness
  Broadmoor: prison for mentally ill criminals

MOUNTAIN MADNESS

6 *Westmorland*: former county of northwest England, now Cumbria

7 *cairn*: small pile of stones erected as a landmark

8 *fell*: stretch of moorland on a hill or mountain

JOHNNY ONE-EYE

14 *derby hat*: bowler hat

15 *D.A.*: District Attorney
   extortion guy: a person who obtains money by force
   lawbooks: lawyer
   indictment: criminal charge

16 *Troy*: city in New York State
   rooty-toot-toot: gun
   tattooing: riddling with bullets
   crockets his monogram: engraves his insignia (crockets = crochets)
   rocking chair: electric chair
   Sing Sing: state prison near New York

17 *blats*: newspapers

18 *croaker*: doctor

19 *rummed up*: drunk (full of rum)
   glaum: look
   duke: hand
   bum lamp: useless eye

20 *nickel*: 5 cent piece
   moo: a pun: the word can mean either 'milk' or 'money'. Here it refers to money.

24 *come-alongs*: handcuffs
25 *square rattle*: fair deal
    on the sneaksby: sneaking
    glim: eye
    dope: expect
    lily: without equal
26 *chalks out*: dies
    icing: getting rid of

TONY KYTES

38 *ferrets*: half-tamed variety of polecat used for driving
    rabbits out of burrows
39 *nunnywatch*: fix, dilemma
    miff: fuss
40 *swound*: swoon

AND MAN

47 *mush*: cornmeal that would be made into porridge
49 *Armenians*: people from Armenia, a ·region northeast of
    Turkey, now called the Armenian Soviet Socialist
    Republic

DEATH OF THE ZULU

52 *Tobruk*: Libyan port, of great strategic importance in
    World War Two
    cobalt: greenish-blue
54 *mealie*: corn
55 *maize*: corn
    cob: the 'head' of corn on which grow the grains or
    kernels
    induna: headman or senior councillor
    Aesculapius: Roman god of medicine, whose emblem is a
    staff with a snake coiled round it
60 *Afrikaans*: language of the Afrikaner people of South
    Africa

THE ROCKING-HORSE WINNER

65 *Ascot, Lincoln (plus St Leger, Grand National & Derby)*:
    famous British horse-races

Notes

65 *batman*: personal servant of an officer
    blade: sharp-witted, dashing, often reckless person
66 *Nat Gould*: Nathaniel Gould wrote 130 sporting novels,
    many of them about horse-racing
69 *writ*: court order (to pay debts)
73 *right as a trivet*: perfectly all right (a 'trivet' was a three-
    legged stand on which hot dishes were placed, hence
    the original expression 'as steady as a trivet')

MR KAPLAN'S WHITE BANNER

76 *halcyon*: idyllic
79 *casuistry*: false reasoning

THE VERGER

83 *verger*: church official who serves as caretaker, usher and
    general attendant
    alpaca: lightweight cloth derived from the hair of the
    alpaca, an animal similar to a llama
    chancel: area of the church in which the altar and com-
    munion table are situated
    genuflect: half-kneel in reverence
    cassock: long tunic worn by the clergy
84 *crook*: bend, curve
    surpliced: covered by a surplice, a loose white linen
    garment with white sleeves
    refectory table: long narrow table previously used in the
    dining-hall of a monastery or convent
85 *in service*: employed as a servant
89 *gilt-edged securities*: safe investments

FIRST CONFESSION

91 *porter*: ale
94 *penitential psalms*: a group of seven psalms that express
    repentance
    caffler: (caviller) one who quibbles or argues
95 *biretta*: square cap worn by Roman Catholic clergy
97 *da*: dad
98 *jay!*: dialectal form of 'jee!' or 'gee whizz!'
99 *bullseye*: large round hard sweet shaped like the bull's-eye
    of a target

THE BOTTOMLESS WELL

102   *bourbon*: whisky

      CCC: Civilian Conservation Corps, a federal agency that administers projects for the conservation of natural resources

      spelunker: cave-explorer

104   *sassafras*: North American tree with soft yellow wood

107   *spatulate*: narrow at one end, broad at the other, and rounded like a spoon

      salamander: type of lizard

113   *risible*: laughable, ridiculous

TO BUILD A FIRE

114   *Yukon*: major North American river that flows through Yukon territory, across Alaska, and into the Bering Strait

      chechaquo: Indian word for tenderfoot, an inexperienced newcomer

115   *divide*: ridge of high ground between two rivers

116   *jowl*: flesh of the lower jaw

117   *niggerhead*: dark-coloured clump of vegetation in a swamp

128   *Mercury*: messenger of the gods in Roman mythology, usually depicted with winged sandals and helmet.

Teacher's Note

Reading Aloud

These stories are usually best enjoyed when read aloud by the teacher or a good reader, with the class following the text. The reading should be strong and uninterrupted, bringing out where necessary the dialectal flavour, such as a slight American drawl in *Johnny One-Eye*. Difficult vocabulary can be simplified (eg by substituting 'half-kneel in reverence' for 'genuflect' in *The Verger*) and technical terms can be explained succinctly without breaking the flow of the story. Obscure references are explained in the Notes and can be jotted down in the teacher's copy before the lesson.

Discussion

This need not follow immediately, but after a short cathartic pause. If the story has had a strong emotional impact it is sometimes better to leave discussion until the following day, although in one or two instances the meaning will have to be elucidated. Each story should be read at one sitting and, where possible, timed to coincide with the end of the lesson. A page takes about $2-2\frac{1}{2}$ minutes to read aloud.

Written Work

Pupils should not be asked to write slavish summaries of the stories, nor to perform a critical autopsy on each. A better method is to ask for the *occasional* résumé or oral account of a similar incident that pupils may have experienced. Discussion of form and technique should be minimal: the story should be regarded primarily as a vehicle of meaning with a bearing on life. This volume is intended for use with *Excellence in English* Book 4 (Hodder & Stoughton) and follow-up exercises can be found there.

Acknowledgments

Thanks are due to the following for permission to include stories in this volume:

Curtis Brown Ltd for THE MAN WHO WASN'T SCARED by Andrew Garve; Mr Tom Hopkinson for MOUNTAIN MADNESS; Constable & Co and the J B Lippincott Co for JOHNNY ONE-EYE from *Runyon from First to Last* by Damon Runyon; Macmillan & Co for TONY KYTES from *Life's Little Ironies* by Thomas Hardy; Faber & Faber for AND MAN from *The Best Stories of William Saroyan*; Mr Uys Krige for DEATH OF THE ZULU; the Estate of the late Mrs Frieda Lawrence & William Heinemann Ltd for THE ROCKING-HORSE WINNER from *The Complete Short Stories of D H Lawrence*; Harcourt, Brace & Co Inc for MR KAPLAN'S WHITE BANNER from *The Education of Hyman Kaplan* by Leo Rosten; William Heinemann Ltd and Doubleday & Co Inc for THE VERGER from *Cosmopolitans* by W Somerset Maugham; A D Peters Ltd for FIRST CONFESSION by Frank O'Connor; John Murray Ltd for THE BOTTOMLESS WELL by Walter S Terry; the Estate of Jack London for TO BUILD A FIRE by Jack London.

I should also like to thank my wife for her unstinting help in the preparation of this book.